INKY FO

INKY FOOT

Award-winning entries
from the 1996
W H Smith
Young Writers' Competition

MACMILLAN
CHILDREN'S BOOKS

First published 1997 by
Macmillan Children's Books
a division of Macmillan Publishers Ltd
25 Eccleston Place, London SW1W 9NF
and Basingstoke
Associated companies throughout the world

ISBN 0 330 35007 2

Text and illustrations copyright © W H Smith Ltd 1997

1 3 5 7 9 8 6 4 2

A CIP catalogue record for this book is available from the British Library.

Phototypeset by Intype London Ltd
Printed by Mackays of Chatham plc, Chatham, Kent.

CONTENTS

INTRODUCTION

Each year the Young Writers' Competition Award Ceremony allows me the privilege of meeting the many young writers whose work I savour in the ensuing anthology. The vitality and enthusiasm for language expressed by the young writers is reflected in the inspirational quality of their work. Often moving, always thought-provoking, we are given a unique insight into the hopes, experiences and concerns of young writers through the freedom of creative expression. When you consider that this year alone over 30,000 entries were received from ardent young authors and poets, their achievement is considerable.

From Michelle Long's witty portrayal of marriage as a football match in *Match of the Day*, to the haunting encounter depicted in Sam Robinson's *Remembering Christie*, from Musa Okwonga's powerful vision of inner city life to Ellen Coffey's invigorating description of a day's *Sledging*, each piece of work in this anthology will absorb the imagination. Each one of us will feel an empathy with one or more of the young writers and poets, as we acknowledge emotions and imaginings we have ourselves experienced in our own childhood. *Inky Foot 1996* is a celebration of young people's huge enthusiasm for the written word, an enthusiasm expressed through an exuberant diversity of language and form, brought together by the strength of the writers' convictions.

Whilst the Young Writers' Competition recognises the achievement of young writers and poets, it also works to support the contribution of teachers and parents in promoting writing, both at school and in the home. The young writers represented in this anthology, together with the hundreds who have been encouraged by certificates of commendation, have achieved success through the love of literature harboured by their families and the energetic dedication of their teachers in creating an environment in which keen readers and writers flourish. It is the continued devotion of families and teachers that ensures the growing success of the Competition each year.

It is particularly rewarding for young entrants that their work is appraised by a distinguished panel of judges, led by Poet Laureate Ted Hughes. Many of the judges have been allied to the Young Writers' Competition since the competition began in 1959, and it is to these judges that we must now offer our thanks. Reading thousands of manuscripts sent in from all over the country, their stamina for a well-loved task must not be underestimated. Hundreds of young writers have received awards and commendations for their work with many past winners, such as Marina Warner, Jan Mark, Glyn Maxwell and Brian Keenan, going on to become well-known authors and journalists in their own right.

While the Young Writers' Competition seeks to support the development of young people through the arts, W H Smith is also concerned about the problems and worries faced by young people through their growing years. To tackle these issues the staff at W H Smith Retail have nominated ChildLine as their Charity of the Year for 1996. ChildLine provides emotional support via the country's only free national helpline for children in trouble or danger. It provides a telephone counselling service for any child with a problem 24 hours a day, every day. Since its launch ten years ago by Esther Rantzen, it has given comfort, advice and protection to more than 600,000 children around the country. We are very proud to be associated with a charity that works so tirelessly to promote the best interests of children everywhere.

Calls are answered by trained counsellors who find ways of sorting out each problem and worry. All calls are treated in complete confidence, unless the child wishes ChildLine to contact someone on their behalf or is in great danger. Each day up to 10,000 children try to call ChildLine, but a lack of funds means that currently only 3,000 of their calls can be answered. W H Smith is committed to helping ChildLine answer more calls. *Stressed Out*, a recent report produced by ChildLine and supported by W H Smith, showed that as many as 79 per cent of secondary school children worry about exams and schoolwork "more than anything else in their lives".

As well as raising awareness of the difficulties children face at school, W H Smith is supporting ChildLine in many different ways, including pledging to raise £150,000 in 1996/7 to help ChildLine meet the cost of answering calls from children on school-related issues. 75 pence from the sale of each copy of *Inky Foot 1996* will be donated directly to ChildLine. It therefore seems particularly appropriate that this most enjoyable celebration of young people's achievement will benefit more young people, helping them to overcome their concerns and problems, whether at school or at home.

Jeremy Hardie
Chairman, W H Smith Group

Advisory judging panel 1996: Ted Hughes (Chairman), Michael Baldwin, Malorie Blackman, Adèle Geras, Mick Gowar, Janni Howker, Jan Mark, Michael Morpurgo.

Preliminary judging panel 1996: Lynn Barclay, Charlotte Brooke-Smith, Richard Brookfield, Linda Hoare, Anna Hopewell, Tariq Latif, Barry Maybury, Richard Quarshie, Timothy Rogers, Betty Rosen, Professor Harold Rosen, Tony Weeks-Pearson.

OVER THE RAINBOW...

Anouska Andre (17)

Naomi Hamilton (6)

The Sweetie Jar

This is a sweetie jar
full of sweets.
There are pink ones and blue ones
and rainbow ones for treats.

I like to share them with my friend, Alex.
I like Alex more than sweets.
She lasts longer
and I feel stronger
when I'm with Alex.

This is a sweetie jar
crowded with sweets.
I like the chewy ones,
egg-shaped and sugary.
They are yummy in my tummy.

Alex and I hide our sweets
under my pillow
for midnight feasts.
They taste better in the night
under the duvet with a night light.
I like it when Alex stays the night.

The sweetie jar is like a story
crammed with lovely things.
Pink and blue and red,
sherbet in my bed.

Eleanora Bryant (13)

*The Hiccup

I came home on Friday,
and before I had even put down my bag,
she came and hugged me.

She said the usual,
how was your day?
do you have homework?
and then,
"they've found a lump."

I didn't cry,
it sounded like a soap opera,
this was my cue to start bawling,
I sat and thought

I know it was my turn for bad luck,
I'd been on a high,
too many good marks,
I'd almost expected it.

And then I cried,
not proper tears,
it just seemed the right thing to do,
to show her I cared.

I do care,
I love her more than anything,
but I didn't need to shed my tears,
not then.

Eleanora Bryant (13)

From then on,
when I hugged her really tight,
she cried,
it reminded me of one of those dolls.

My sister jumped in,
she came around and bawled,
because that's what she does.
I don't.

Then she was in hospital,
I made her a card,
it was a nice room,
with a view of London.

I played with the stethoscope,
I heard my heart,
and my Dad's,
and my sister's.

I know it's my fault,
I wanted something to happen,
something interesting,
so that when I wrote I had something to say.

Then she came home,
Interflora called twice
with huge bouquets of flowers,
one from her work and the other from my sister.

I told her if I had the money,
I'd buy her every flower on the earth.

Daniel O'Rourke (13)

Aidan Rush (11)

*Ebley Under 11s

"Right, lads, I want you to win."
We won't.
"Tim, you're doing really well."
He isn't.
"You only let 3 goals in last week."
Exactly.
"Aidan, you'll be up front."
I know I'm going to be substituted.

"Paul, you're playing well, doing lots of passes."
He isn't.
"You're not just running around like a warthog."
He is.
"I counted how many times you passed last week."
So did I. He didn't.

The half-time whistle blows.
We're losing 3–1
and he is going to say,
Aidan, you're substituted.

"Well done, lads. Richard, you've scored."
Yes. A two yard, off-side tap-in.
"Tim, you've made some great saves."
In training.
"Aidan, you're substituted."

David Newman (11)

*Righting the Writing?

The problem with my *typewriter* is that when you press the letter "o", you get a hole in your paper. The letter "p" always lands too close to the letter before it and about a millimetre higher up on the page than all the other letters on the same line. The "caps" key tends to get stuck so it's best not to use capital letters . . . and since you can't tell the difference between a comma and a full stop, your story makes *more* sense if you use neither.

The problem with my *family* is that they don't see this as a problem. Nobody ever seems to *listen* to me. Not even Grandma . . . And Mam says Grandma *spoils* me.

Grandma says *she* had to write with chalk on a slate, Mam says there was a guy in the sixties called e.e. cummings who never used capital letters anyway, and Dad just sent me a black felt tip pen that he got free in a music mag, so I could draw in the missing bits. It's got an italic nib so the print looks a bit odd but it does play doh, ray, me, fah, soh, lah, te, if you hold it upside down. My stepdad Pete did peer at his "Ban the bomb/ Peace and Love" medallion long enough to tell me that he used to write all his letters by hand and sign them all "luv and peas". Then he tossed his *un*trendy long hair back over his shoulders, told me that Dylan never used a word processor and offered to lend me his Joan Baez tapes. Again.

I tell you, they've no idea. I am a child of the *nineties* . . . not the *sixties*. I'll be 16 in the year 2000 and I bet by then I could open up our house as a museum.

My needs are sophisticated. I need a state of the art, multimedia PC and things in my house are more state of

8

the *ark*. And they just don't understand. I bet the longest thing my Grandma ever had to write was a shopping list and as for this e.e. cummings man, even if Mam's right about him and the small letters, I'll bet *he* never went to *my* school. At least, if he did, he most certainly *did not* have *my* English teacher. No way. As for Dad, at least he was being creative so I don't have the heart to tell him that the top "doh" is missing from the pen, and it nearly got me thrown out of music. It wasn't the missing "doh" that caused the bother, it was the class really. You see, every time I started to write, the pen sang doh, ray, me, fah, soh, lah, te ... and nearly everybody in the class yelled an out of tune "doh", to round things off so to speak. It got to the point when even Miss was doing it, although she sang the "doh" in tune, or at least as in tune as you can be with something that sounds like a cross between Sooty's xylophone and a musical Christmas card. Anyway, that's what finally got her rattled I think. And even if it hadn't done, the pen writes *black* and my typewriter ... when it does bother to ink the letters, does them in *blue*.

Now I know that none of this should matter. I know it doesn't actually stop me writing. But it certainly does distract me. So it *is* a problem and it's a problem I've been thinking about a lot lately. It's a real handicap to someone like me. Someone with real potential. I need something *futuristic*. *Adequate* would do. Something that would help me fulfil my natural potential. Tchaikovsky had already composed great works by the time he was my age! He'll have had the right equipment though. I bet he never had a piano with keys missing. Can you imagine him writing a symphony using just three notes because the others didn't work? Never. It's like Bach's Air on a G string. He *did* have other strings you know.

I'm nearly eleven now and my career and development

are being restricted by substandard equipment. Think about it . . .

Who ever got rich and famous for a novel with no punctuation, barely legible and with holes in the pages? A budding author deserves help. What is the point in my being a creative genius if I lack the technological support to exploit my skills? What if Tchaikovsky had been told to go off and compose on a kazoo? What if his Mam had said "Here you are son, a comb and a sheet of tissue paper, get yourself away and compose a quick sonata . . ."

I could be the next Shakespeare . . . Charles Dickens . . . Ted Hughes even . . . I could even win the school Creative Writing Competition . . . And *that* was my ambition at the moment.

You see, winning the prize meant a trip to *Disneyland* and getting published in the local paper. I could be *famous*. It could be the start of my career and it was time I got things started. I wasn't getting any younger. Michael Jackson was performing in public long before he was eleven. Really I had no time to waste.

Miss told us about it in Assembly which is not always a good time for me. Usually I sleep through assemblies. Not that anyone can tell. It's the sort of sleep you do with your eyes open. So you look as if you're there but you're not really. Sometimes I think I can really leave my body sitting there while I do other things like finish the last chapter of the book Mam made me put down at 1.15 am last night. I think about this a lot and keep trying to do it but as yet I've not actually managed. I think I've imagined I've done it, but sometimes I get the ending of the story wrong so maybe it's just that I sort of dreamt it. Anyway, today I was awake on account of my haircut. Mam attacked me with the scissors last night. (We're on an economy drive so the Hairdresser's is out.) And then, just to make things even worse, Grandma leapt on me

with Grandad's new shaver and decided she should shave
my neck. She seemed to think it was a great treat using
Grandad's new shaver and maybe it was for her. But it
wasn't for me. I tried to tell her that it might be new to
him, but it wasn't to me since he used it on his stubble
every day. I can tell you, my Grandad is pretty stubbly. (I
could also tell you that Grandma spends nearly every day
at Oxfam, Save the Children, Scope or Sue Rider and
Grandad's new razor is probably not really all that new
to him either . . .) Anyway, I was awake worrying about
people noticing and Miss explained a bit about the competition and said that presentation went nine tenths of the
way to success. She was definitely looking at me when she
said that, and I wasn't sure if she was remembering my
project on dogs or wondering why I was trying to make
my head disappear into my shirt collar. Maybe she just
thought my neck was shrinking. With the rain or something. My project had been terrific but it did have a sort
of moth-eaten look about it on account of the holey "o"s.
Maybe she was warning me . . . She said the poster had
been put up in reception so I decided to go after school
to get a proper look, when nobody else was around. I
couldn't wait . . . By ten past four I'd memorised every
line.

"Do you have an eccentric family? If so, we want to
hear about it. In 3000 words or less describe your
family to the rest of the school."

Brilliant. Just what I wanted. I just *knew* I could do
that. I dashed straight home. Perhaps I could get the type
writer to behave a bit better . . .
Mam was engrossed taking "reduced" stickers off her
latest bargains when I got in. (Dad says she'll buy anything
that's reduced. But did we really need so many bashed tins

11

of peas?) No point in mentioning the typewriter again, I could tell. Also she might want me to cut saver coupons off for her if I hung about.

"I'm staying in, Mam . . . if anyone calls . . ." She didn't ask why so I didn't explain. In fact she didn't bother to answer at all. Sometimes I think I could completely disappear and nobody would notice. They'll notice me all right when I win this competition. Some people think it's soppy to be interested in school things . . . Football's OK but writing tends to get you scoffed at. It's stupid really because at least with writing there's no chance of breaking a leg or getting your head kicked in.

I rolled a sheet of beautiful white, silky, clean paper into the carriage and took a deep breath. Maybe if I was really gentle . . .

My Mam thinks her Mini is a Time Machine. It isn't. But it's best not to tell her that. Well, not straight out anyway.

"It's definitely seen better times, that car . . ." is what Grandad says. But Grandad says that about lots of things. It's to do with being a grandad. They always think things were better in the past, have you noticed that? And they say it in a way that's supposed to make you believe they're right. They're not of course . . .

. . . Especially if they are talking about typewriters! It's just not fair. I'd done five lines and so far I had six holes, twenty-one missing letters, thirteen handwritten punctuation marks in blue/black and the beautiful paper was getting chewed up at the edges because the carriage was so stiff. Maybe Mam would iron the page? I've seen her iron her hair to try to straighten it so she might be able to do something with this. Grandma would definitely be able to. She irons all sorts of things does Grandma. Even my entry for the Art competition once, after Mam made it go all crinkly from drying it in the airing cupboard when the paint wouldn't dry. She has bother with wet things, my Mam. Pete bought her a mobile phone so she could talk, wash up *and* cook all at the *same* time. He says it's stopped her wasting *time* yapping . . . Now she just wastes *money*. She dropped it in the bath with Grandma on the other end. I can just imagine the bubbles coming to the surface and frothing while Grandma chunters away complaining and coughing and spluttering. Mam put it in the Aga to dry and Pete said it would need more than Grandma ironing it to put it to rights. Chuntering by the way is a cross between chattering and uttering, though I don't know where the spare "n" comes from. Grandmas do it a lot.

A budding author deserves the best equipment money can buy and that's the problem, according to Mam. We don't have the money to do the buying. Everything in our house is prehistoric. Come to think of it everything outside is too. Our garage is nearly a listed building. Some people have garages that open with an electronic code. Ours won't open with brute force. You have to put a brick beside the door to keep it closed and when you do manage to lock it, it jams. Then you have to run at it and kick it karate style when it's least expecting you, and Pete has the nerve to call it an "up and over door". What he actually means is that you run at it, jump up, kick the handle and on a good day the lock unjams and the door flips over. Like I said – "up and over". You do the "upping" and on a good day (usually in the summer – it doesn't like wet), it does the "overing".

Then there's Mam's car. I should put that in my story.

Mam's car sort of matches our garage. The windows get stuck if you wind them down too far and one is really only half a window anyway. You can't tell though if you keep the window jammed closed. You see, Dad fitted her a wing mirror as a surprise one Christmas and he wound the window down inside the door before he drilled the hole to fix the mirror. The problem was that he drilled the hole in the bit of door where the glass was wound down into so the bottom part of the window got shattered. You can imagine what a surprise Mam got that Christmas but she does have a wing mirror now.

I'll have to rephrase that; there's too many "o"s in it for my typewriter. But maybe it's best to get the ideas written down first.

My Mam loves her Mini though. In fact she loves all Minis and the older they are the better she seems to love them. Dad says that Mini owners are strange people. They chug about the place waving and smiling to each other like they are all members of a secret society and like maybe they all know something good about Minis that we don't. She thinks her Mini is beautiful, does my Mam. It's racing green. On the outside anyway. At least most of it is except for the occasional yellow blob. The inside is all yellow. Maybe Mam could only afford to have the outside done and even then only with one coat. You see, the yellow blobs seem to be getting bigger and bigger and Mam'll not let anyone wash her car. Grandad thinks that's because she's scared the paint will wash off and Dad reckons that one night there'll be a great rainstorm and we'll wake up to find the Mini is yellow again. I think he's probably right but I hope I'm not with Mam when it happens. She'll be ever so upset.

14

She thinks it's perfect and she really hates parking in town because bits of the car keep going missing. Mam thinks that her Mini is so lovely that people keep pinching parts off it. I don't like to tell her that me and Dad think it's that bits drop off when she's not looking.

I'll have to remember about the "p"s; they're beginning to pile up, a bit. And there's a great wodge of letters jammed together near the ribbon. It's like they've huddled together for protection because they don't like being bashed against the paper.

Some really famous people have had Minis, Mam says. She means Twiggy and Paul McCartney but THEY'RE not really famous NOW. I try to explain this to her but she doesn't understand, but then why should she? She was forty in September, my Mam, so you see, she's really quite old.

Just like this machine. It's stuck on line twenty-two and I can't tell why. There's no "tab" mark. In fact the little pointer is missing. This is no good at all. I need a word with Grandma in private. She's a bit more forward-thinking than Mam and she's trendier. You know Jarvis Cocker from Pulp? Well him and my Grandma have something in common; they both buy all their clothes from Oxfam. And Grandma *did* try to get Mam to see sense about the car. But maybe that was because of the accident . . . which I think was Mam's fault. (But I keep that a secret.)

You see, Grandma doesn't drive. Well, not from the driving seat anyway. She gives instructions from the passenger seat. Grandad did try to teach her to drive but she kept losing her temper and throwing her licence out of the

15

window, which would have been OK, Grandad said, if people hadn't kept posting it back to her.

Anyway, Grandma's accident happened because of Mam's car which has a cut-off switch to stop people pinching it. (As if anybody would.) Mam puts it on when she leaves the car. Sometimes the car won't start when she gets back even if the switch is off and by the time Mam has flicked it backwards and forwards a few times she can't remember what position it was in when she started. It never seems to occur to her not to bother with the switch. I mean, who else would want Mam's Mini? The last one she had was bad enough and she refused to get rid of it even after she bought this one. She kept telling me (when she was in a good mood) that she was saving it for me but she didn't seem to realise that that *didn't* put *me* in a good mood! Eventually the scrap man took it but we told Mam that we'd given it to a deserving cause. (Pete said the scrap man *was* a deserving cause.) Anyway, Mam parks this one on a hill so she can bump start it, but this time it wouldn't even bump start. So Grandma had to push. I offered but Mam wouldn't let me because it was throwing it down and I'd get wet. Maybe she thinks I'll melt or shrink and Grandma won't . . . Anyway, Grandma was wearing her snood, Mam said. A snood is a sort of baggy woolly hat scarf type thing that goes around your neck and over your head and tends to be worn by Grandmas. Grandma's snood was bright yellow so she's easily seen. A man with a dog came to help push, and every time they managed to get some speed up, the dog started to bark and run in the opposite direction . . . Pretty soon it wouldn't matter that the car wouldn't start because pretty soon they'd have pushed us all the way home. Grandma's snood was starting to slip down over her face and I was starting to worry that maybe my Grandma *was* shrinking. Then Mam remembered the switch. She flicked it, the engine growled into life and I watched Grandma's yellow snood disappear into a great cloud of murky black exhaust fume smoke. A choking noise seemed to come from the engine (or it could have been Grandma) and the Mini sped away, pinning me and Mam back against our seats.

Now I think at this point, if I'd been Mam I'd have just made for home and left Grandma to get the bus because it was pretty obvious that she would not be in a good mood. But no. Yelling to me to climb into the back she told me to hold the door open as we passed Grandma, as if she expected her to leap in Supergran-style while the car was moving. But that was not actually possible. You see, there'd been a slight accident ... The car had shot forwards, plunging Grandma into the smoke. She'd covered her eyes with her snood and somehow managed to trip over the man's left foot which had somehow got entangled with her right one and they had landed together almost (although he was on top), flat out on the ground in the middle of the road. Their attempts to stand up were being greatly hampered by the dog who was busy savaging Grandma's snood. Things did not look good. The man managed to pull his dog off Grandma's head and dashed off.

You see, this could go in my story ... I gave the type writer a shove and glared at it. Mam's head appeared around the door. She looked worried.

"What are *you* doing here?" She sounded really surprised and if I'd wanted to miss tea I'd have told her that I lived here and asked her who she'd expected to find in *my* room. Those bashed cans must have been pretty fascinating. I worry about my Mam sometimes.

"Grandma said for you to go over to her house as soon as you came in ... She's been to some auction ..." I groaned. That usually meant there would be a dozen

17

pairs of "not quite the right shade of grey" (more blue, but they will dye), school pants for me to try on that looked as if they were previously owned by a hippopotamus. Couldn't Mam see I was *busy*?

"She's got you one of those writing processor things . . ." Mam sounded disapproving and I suddenly felt less busy. I made to dash off but Mam hadn't finished.

" . . . I told her, you'd a perfectly good *typewriter* that belonged to your Great Grandad but *nobody ever seems to listen to me . . .*" She shook her head.

"*I always say your Grandma spoils you . . .!*"

Sophie Holland (6)

Felicia Downs-Barton (6)

*Death: A Conversation

I said to Mummy
When I'm a big lady and I go away
I'll let you come to my house
For lunch.

And Mummy said
Oh thank you.

And I said
And when you are dead
I'll be very kind
And put flowers on your grave.

And Mummy said
Hmm, thank you very much indeed.
But what if I don't have a grave?
What if I want to be cremated?

And I said
Oh no
Don't do that
I don't want you to be born as
Something else.
What if you were a fly
And somebody squashed you?

And Mummy said
Not reincarnated – cremated.
It means being roasted until
you become ashes
then the ashes are scattered
Somewhere romantic.

And I said
No, don't do that.
I wouldn't be able to see you any more,
And I might forget you
And I might forget what you look like.
I'm very young so I do forget things.
I forget where to put

My brush.
Anyway they don't do that any more,
It was the Romans and Saxons
years ago when you were just a cell.

And Mummy said
That long ago?
Well as I haven't any plans
To die
Just yet
We're all right, aren't we?

Lucy Hudson (14)

Death on the Ice

To the others, they are simply livelihood.
To me, our trade is murder.
When they stare with their hopeless eyes,
Accepting our cruelty without comment,
Leaving only lingering, crushing guilt.
The sealing boats have left for the ice floes,
To return in three days with three days' catch.

The iceberg is flat and massive; threatening.
The sea reaches hungrily with white, decaying fingers.
Foaming at the mouth, the water smiles silently.
It will be fed soon, its carnivorous stomach filled,
When one young sealer is too cold, too slow, too stiff.
I clutch my wooden club tighter, threatening Mother
    Nature.
I will go only when I am ready, the seals will not claim
    me.

Loneliness kills a man faster than any force of nature.
I have been alone for hundreds of suns and moons.
I have eaten the flesh from the finger of the man next to
    me.
I am curdled with guilt, I have pushed his body away.
The seals' blood has laid out a red carpet for me to walk
    on,
Like royalty, I bow to my subjects and wave a hand,
The material snaps off my sleeve. I lay my head on the
    ice.

Sealing:

Boats took men, young as fourteen, off the coast of St. John's Newfoundland, to the ice floes that arrived in September and only melted in June.

Here the men were released onto the sheet ice wearing inadequate clothes supplied by the traders, and clutching heavy objects.

The men's job was to kill as many seals, which lay basking on the ice, as possible, to supply the growing trade in seal meat.

Horrifically, the boats were often unable to reach the ice floes again, and the sealers were trapped for days, left to die.

Francesca Hails (7)

Questions

What is the sun?
An orange in the sky
Firelight.

Where does it go at night?
It hides behind the clouds
Disappears behind the moon.

What is the sea?
A warm blanket
A bed for mermaids.

Where does the tide go?
It goes to an island
for a lie down.

What is the rain?
Water dripping from the sky
God crying.

Where does it rain?
On my head
On my rabbit in the garden.

What is the earth?
It is our home.
We live there.

BREAKING THE LONG GRASS

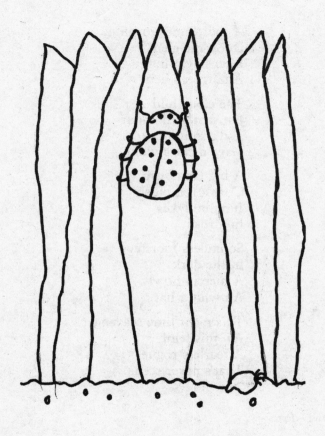

Asni Cook (10)

Mairi McKenna (12)

The Nicht Time Thief

A tod[1] came trottin
Doon the glen,
Efter havin hud
A fairmer's hen.

The clock hud
Jist struck the hour
Tod's shinin een
Gave nicht a glour.

A big lang bush
Coat a red blush
Jumpin dykes
In a rush.

Soondless footsteps
In the dark
A piercin howl
An whit a bark.

This nicht time scavenger
Aw this fein!
A fearless rogue
That's never seen.

1   tod – fox

Mairi McKenna (12)

John Mindham (12)

Danielle Monnier-Hovell (12)

In the Long Grass

A mouse is hiding
In the long grass.
Hiding.

Footsteps are coming
Through the long grass.
Coming.

Move slowly closer,
Parting the long grass.
Closer.

The mouse is running
Under the long grass.
Running.

The footsteps quicken.
Chasing the long grass.
Quicken.

An eye is looking:
Mouse in the long grass!
Looking.

Both running faster,
Breaking the long grass.
Faster.

The gap is closing
Deep in the long grass.
Closing.

Cat getting nearer
Mouse in the long grass.
Nearer.

Pounce.

Caught.

Dead.

Rest in Peace,
Mouse,
In the long grass.

Philip Clack (12)

Caterpillars

One will be . . .
Disguised as a moustache,
Untouched by scissors.
With red and brown hairs,
Which stick out here and there.
Just waiting for the touch of a comb.

Another will be . . .
Tiny and delicate,
Blending in with the grass . . .
You see him,
Then you don't.

The next will be . . .
Green, curled up in a ball,
Hiding from its hunter,
The sharp black crow.

The last will be . . .
Camouflaged with green and brown
Pretending to be a soldier in Vietnam,
Trekking across forests,
Facing pools of quicksand,
And bombs of bird's waste . . .
As the bird swoops over
And homes in on the target.

Run, Rabbit, Run

The children sat in a circle. In the centre burned a bright fire. Each child held a length of wood in his hand. The thin, timber poles were held as steady as possible, with their ends just touching the flames. The whole ring formed a wheel: the fire the hub; the poles the spokes; the children the hoop.

Jona spoke first, his words visible in the frosty night air. "I think we should go soon," he said, his eyes scanning each of the twenty children.

"It *is* cold," someone said.

The oldest boy there, Thomas, groaned. "It is the middle of winter, you know? Whose crazy idea was it to come out here at this time of night?"

Jona grinned – trust Thomas to be pessimistic. But he was right, Jona's parents would be worrying about him, now. "We should come back tomorrow. Everyone remember to bring their coins, OK?"

There were a number of mumbled agreements and nods. Thomas nodded most vigorously, the bobble on his hat bouncing like a maniacal rabbit.

"Good," Jona said, standing. As if on cue, the children stood. In single file, they trudged across the potatoes and cabbages of the allotment and placed their poles in a neat pile beside Jona's father's shed. Jona picked up the blue plastic covering and flung it across the wood. He put a heavy stone on the covering to hold it down and followed the children back to the houses.

During the night rain had fallen and the children found that the allotment was now a sea of mud. Jona hadn't worn his boots and the mud soaked into his sneakers. He tried to walk on dry patches but every so often he would have to walk through the mud.

When he reached the Site his feet were drenched. Only six of the children had turned up; the others having to go to church. Thomas was there, standing proud beside the burnt-out fire, his scarlet wellington boots covered with dark brown mud. As Jona approached, Thomas flicked his coin into the air. Jona rushed forward and jumped into the air, catching the falling coin in his hand.

"Give it back!" Thomas demanded, holding his hand out.

Jona smiled slyly. He placed the coin on his thumb and flicked it into the air. He watched as it floated upwards, spinning over and over. Thomas clasped his hands together to catch the coin as it came down. Jona, mischief taking over his rationality, kicked up some mud onto Thomas's coat. The older boy took his gaze off the coin to see what had happened and the copper disc spiralled down into the mud. There was an oozy splash and then the coin vanished beneath the muck.

Thomas, aware of what Jona had done, glared tempestuously, his face turning the colour of his boots. He crouched in the mud and gingerly slid a hand into the ooze. Jona burst out laughing at the sloshing noise and the other children started chuckling and pointing. Thomas, unable to find his precious coin, thrashed about in the mud, desperately trying to recover the copper circle.

"Looking for your next meal, Tom?" someone behind Jona asked, laughing.

"He's trying to find a nice worm for his dinner!"

"Your house is over there, Thomas, why are you looking down there?"

Thomas stood up suddenly. "Shut up! Shut up, all of you!"

The children weren't afraid of the older boy even though he was several centimetres taller than any of them.

Thomas clenched his hand into a fist and lunged at Jona. The younger boy dodged the thrust but slipped in the mud. Arms windmilling, Jona plunged into the mud, spraying it over the other children.

Now it was Thomas's turn to laugh, at Jona and the others. He roared and pointed, his face split almost in half by his broad smile. Jona lay in the mud, bewildered and upset, wondering what had happened. He slowly picked himself up. When Thomas saw Jona's mud-enveloped clothes he laughed even harder.

"Not funny!" Jona blurted, shaking the mud off his hands. "Stop laughing!"

A look of contempt passed across Thomas's face as Jona ordered him to silence. His red face had paled but the smile was still there; mocking, scorning, taunting. His muddy boots stamped the mud as he tried to keep warm. "Rabbit."

Jona started. He hadn't been called that name since he had been in primary school. *They* had likened him with a rabbit: scared, cautious, always fleeing when trouble cropped up. He remembered the little scrawled chalk pictures of rabbits on the wall outside his house, the taunting from the older children in the playground.

"Shut up!" Jona spat, taking a step towards Thomas.

The older boy stood still, hands on hips, daring the youngster to start a fight. "Rabbit, bunny rabbit."

Jona's hands clenched. He forced himself to open them; he didn't want to pick a fight with Thomas. The older boy was obnoxious and deserved to have his brains knocked out, but someone of the same age, the same height would have to carry out the righteous act.

He turned and stamped away from the group of children. He heard Thomas's scornful laughter behind him. Mustn't let him provoke you, can't give in to his stupid pranks! Well, damn him, why should he laugh at me?

Jona stopped and crouched, pretending to tie the laces on his shoes. With his right hand he slowly scooped up a handful, shielding it from Thomas's view with his body. He stood, took a step forward and turned quickly on his heel. His arm shot out towards Thomas, the mud flying through the air.

The older boy didn't have time to dodge: the mud hit him square in the face, trickled into his open mouth. For a second everyone was silent. Then all hell broke loose. Thomas' friends in the assembled group rounded on Jona, one or two helped Thomas wipe the mud from his face.

Jona turned and ran. The mud slipped by beneath his shoes. He hoped that he could keep his grip and not fall head first into the ooze again. Thomas and his friends were hot on Jona's heels as he reached the wire fence that separated the allotment from the houses.

His numb fingers gripped the cold wire mesh and he started to climb. He looked back and saw the gang of children right behind him. His progress was irritatingly slow and he strained his arms to pull himself closer to the top of the fence. His slippery shoes made climbing even harder and he wasn't surprised when he felt someone tug on the back of his trousers.

The fear of getting caught gave Jona an extra boost of strength and his hand clenched around the wire at the top of the fence. He heaved himself up, swung his leg over the top. Pulling his other leg over he stared straight into Thomas's muddy face. The boy had murder in his eyes.

Jona dropped down onto the concrete pavement. He heard something rip and saw that a length of his coat had torn on a loose wire. He had no time to worry as the older boys were cresting the fence.

He sprinted down the pavement, his sneakers squelching with each step. From behind he heard grunts and shouts of "rabbit". He sure felt like a rabbit right now, running from a pack of hounds. He was the rabbit and he had to find his warren where he would be safe. If he couldn't reach his warren before the hounds caught him . . . he dreaded to think what they would do to him.

To keep his mind off the thought, he sang a song to himself. He could hear his own voice clearly in his head although no one else was able to. *Run, rabbit, run, rabbit, run, run, run.* Each beat came with a pace.

His eyes caught on something ahead; the shiny roofs of the factories. He was nearly home! Just another couple of hundred yards and then he would turn right. Down that road and then left, and he would be home. And safe.

The plumes of dark smoke poured from the factory chimneys and formed foreboding devils and witches in the sky. They seemed to be jeering at him, pointing fingers, whispering evil things.

He wanted to get home even sooner, now. What with devils and witches in front of him and a pack of vicious dogs behind, he felt boxed in. His mind went to the rabbit at the bottom of his garden, sitting all alone in his cage. Floppy didn't know how lucky he was in his little hutch, safe from predators and the outside world. How grateful he would be if he could realise that he had been done a huge favour when Jona's family brought him from the pet shop.

Jona turned and ran down the road to his right. The houses that lined each side of the street seemed like monsters huddled together. Their white teeth and shining eyes pierced his vision and he closed his eyes. Still the sound of snarling dogs and cackling witches filled his ears.

When he at last opened his eyes he was at the corner of his street. He crossed the road quickly not looking behind in fear that he would see huge slobbering dogs, with their gleaming white teeth and their powerful paws.

Run, rabbit, run rabbit.

Number two, with the cracked slates. Number four, with the peeling front door. Number six, with the boarded-up windows. Number eight, with the loose gate. Number ten, with the crumbling brick wall. Number twelve, his house.

Run, run, run.

Number twelve sparkled and shined. The bright blue paint of the door and gate with its heavenly radiance. The inviting doormat, the clear panes of glass in the windows. The magnificent Elysium of the warren.

Don't let the farmer . . .

Something caught him on the back of the neck. Jona toppled forward, his balance gone. He smacked into the pavement and felt something give in his nose. Delicately putting a hand to his face, he felt something warm trickle from his nostrils. He pushed himself up slowly, shaking his head to clear his vision.

A hand gripped his hair and jerked his head up. Jona gave a squeal of pain and stood. He was spun around, and looked into Thomas's face.

"I'm going to crack your head open, rabbit!" the dog barked. For some reason the dog had mud on its snout. Jona tried hard to figure out why but he couldn't quite recall what had happened.

A moment later, more dogs appeared and surrounded the rabbit. Spittle dripped from their jaws, and they sniffed and growled at the little bunny rabbit. Their beady eyes were alive with fire as they watched their leader hold the prey.

"Let me go, you're hurting me!" the rabbit pleaded.

"No," the dog barked. "I caught you and now I'm going to do you!"

36

"No!" the rabbit implored. "Please let me go!"

"Why should I?"

"'Cause I'm sorry for throwing mud in your face!"

The dog smarted with that. A paw came up and wiped some mud from the dog's muzzle. "I'm going to rip you apart, rabbit!"

Suddenly, it all came back. The rabbit and dogs vanished and Jona was standing before Thomas and his cronies.

Without thinking, Jona lashed out and punched Thomas in the face. Thomas reeled backwards, his friends stepping forward. Another fist shot out and again Thomas staggered back. The other kids didn't move forward but watched as Thomas swung his arms wildly in an attempt to protect himself.

But Jona was mad now, and Thomas's feeble efforts couldn't help him from falling onto the ground with another punch.

Seeing that this was his chance to escape, Jona turned and ran to his house, throwing open the door and charging inside.

The fire blazed high. The children sat around the flames, holding thin wooden poles into the heat. They talked for a long time, about school, girls, boys, football and other popular things.

When the fire burned out they tramped across the allotment, a line of solemn monks going to church in single file. The moon was bright when they reached the shed. They laid the poles in a pile. A blue sheet was thrown over the wood to protect it from the rain.

They left silently. Ten wooden poles beside the shed, ten charred poles in the remains of the fire. The mud had dried during the day and it no longer sloshed about beneath their feet. In the dry dirt there sat a single, copper coin. No one saw it as they left for their homes.

The rabbit had gone, moved on to another warren, another life. The dog had stayed, but never barked again, silent for ever.

Stop running, rabbit. You can stop running, now.

Sam Keeble (5)

*When I'm Hungry

When I'm hungry my mouth
is as big as a brown bear's.
I get monster teeth and
a lion roars in my tummy.
Mummy says, "Go and wash your hands!"

Amy Robertson (8)

Daniel Brown (10)

A Bird Lay Dead

A bird lay dead
outside my house.
There was blood,
and its wings were spread out.
I knew I had to move it.
If my sister had seen it
she would have cried.
I went round the back
and got a shovel.
I scooped it into an old box.
I clutched the box under one arm.
I had the shovel in the other hand.
I went to the garden
where my Dad grew veg.
I dug a hole beneath some rockery.
I put the stones back
and made a cross
where the dead bird lay.

Each new month
I laid some flowers.

Stevie Crowther (10)

Kathleen Wainwright (9)

Jiwawa and the Talking Rhino

Jiwawa was a young girl. She lived in a tribe along with her family.

Jiwawa was no ordinary girl. As the men and boys went hunting, Jiwawa would follow them and whisper in the prey's ear:

"Run run! The warriors come come!
And they are dum dum!
They will kill you with their gun gun!"

Sometimes the creatures would run but those who did not died.

One day, Jiwawa was playing with her friend, Finna. They were dancing on a large sheet on top of some beans, when suddenly Yoko, a youth who was learning to be a warrior, came running up.

"Jiwawa! Finna! We are catching a rhino today!" began Yoko. "Would you like to come with us? You'd watch of course. Moca and Nala are watching also, please come! It could be so fun!"

Finna quickly agreed.

"You expect me to go and see a rhino be slaughtered? HUH!!!" screamed Jiwawa, and she ran off in the direction of the rhino.

As her hips began to get sore, Jiwawa stopped running. In front of her was the vast open African plain, reaching as far as she could see in any direction. Jiwawa lifted her arm up in the air and sang a sweet tune, for her heart was full of happiness.

Then coming out of the distance, there was a huge grey beast. It was charging at about 10 m.p.h. towards Jiwawa. Sand and rubble were flying everywhere. Occasionally, a tuft of dry grass would fly up into the air, and get caught by a sudden gasp of wind.

The rhino was now rather close, and Jiwawa could feel its feet pumping the ground and shaking it roughly. She turned her head and found a tall tree that was very easy to climb. She fled towards it, and was soon high up above the eaves. Jiwawa soon found that it was a mango tree and was soon eating ripe mangoes by the second.

Nothing moved, only her heart slowly pumping blood around her body; it sprinted around her stomach. At last the rhino stopped at the foot of the tree. Its huge snout lifted up into the air and sniffed it. Could it smell her?

Then it suddenly began to chant:

"COME DOWN, FRIEND!
Jiwawa Jiwawa Jiwawa.
I WILL NOT HURT YOU!
Jiwawa Jiwawa Jiwawa.
YOU ARE KINDLY!
Jiwawa Jiwawa Jiwawa."

Jiwawa's heart stopped suddenly. She looked through the leaves at the rhino. It whispered "Come down! Come down!" over and over again.

Jiwawa slowly climbed down the tree, her heart in her mouth.

"Friend, Jiwawa, friend!" whispered the rhino. "Come on my back, and I will take you back back!"

Jiwawa slowly climbed on the rhino's back. Slowly and quietly, the rhino took her home. Few people noticed her, and everyone was silent. Jiwawa was always friends with the rhino. As they often sat together under the eaves of the mango tree.

One day, Jiwawa and her rhino were sitting under the mango tree, when some British men in black overalls came with huge roaring chainsaws and baskets ready to pluck the mangoes. A few of the men had guns, they sent a shiver down her spine.

As the men advanced towards Jiwawa they noticed the rhino.

"Keep still! There's a rhino sitting by you! It could attack any second!!!" screamed the men.

"My rhino will not harm any one apart from you!" screamed Jiwawa. "And this is my tree, you can't have any of my mangoes! And you definitely can't chop it down, so you can go now or I'll set my rhino on you!"

The men stared at her in bewilderment, their eyes almost

dropped out. Her rhino put its head down and scratched the floor with its front leg.

"GO!" screamed Jiwawa.

The men's feet seemed to be glued to the ground.

"You promissssssssse thatttt you will nnnnnnot sssss-ssetttt yourrrrr rhinno onnnn us?" asked the men. They were too scared to talk properly.

"Do I look like the kind of person who would break a promise?" asked Jiwawa.

Silence.

"Well do I?" asked Jiwawa once again.

"No," said one of the bravest of the men.

"GOOD! Be off!!" said Jiwawa.

The men quickly ran off and Jiwawa and the rhino were always safe for the rest of their lives.

DON'T WANT TO DO THIS

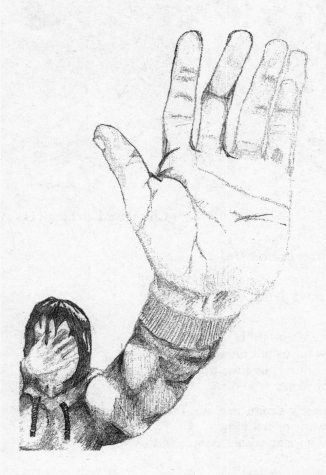

David Aldhouse (15)

Charlotte Latcham (11)

Sarah Beaton (16)

Views from a Park Bench

There's a family walking past
I want to tell them
– Value your time together
  I won't

There's a man in a suit on a mobile phone
I want to tell him
– There are other people in this world
  I won't

There's a couple arguing
I want to tell them
– It really isn't worth it
  I won't

There's a man collapsing from "mid-morning" drinking
I want to tell him
– There's hope for everyone
  I won't

There's a girl with perfect hair, face, figure
I want to tell her
– A broken nail isn't the end of the world
  I won't

There's a telephone box
I want to tell my family
– I am alive
  I can't.

Musa Okwonga (16)

**Crime Pays?

Why am I telling you this now? OK – it's not for your
benefit, I don't even know you. I do it because I need
to get this down. I guess I'm not safe anywhere but in
retrospect.

I'm sitting somewhere in humid North London; the
afternoon is slow, brown and frugal with it, since it can't
afford the sun. Something creamy is lying around my
ankles: the carpet or a maligned blanket. Or perhaps just
the dog. And Otieno? Otieno's gone, he's been gone for a
long time now. So have I – we both ran together, me a lot
faster, but he was all right, just a total packer. He'll survive.

Otieno. 6'2", brightish, ambitiousissimi, sought Law
degree at Leicester, whatever, wherever that was. He was
so restrained, conformist; fitted the legal profession to a
QC. Raised under gavel and inquisition (literally! his dad
was the regional judge!) in a village, left-turn-at-Jinja.
Imported 1984, four, with a pair of cheap moccasins and
a sackful of cassava seeds. When we lost it, up here, a
couple of months ago, I lost less than he did, reason,
control. When you're as placid as he was the swing from
calm to hysteria is almost criminal. You see, of the two of
us, he was ultramoral. He came up with the eulogies on
guilt, aggression, poll tax, had a pithy mental paragraph
for everything. But maybe he never really lost it: I got
involved, I hated this guy, but Otieno just did it, simple,
like locking the front door, putting the lid back on the
jam.

(He did weights, like me, but *real weights*, not just one
or two, bundles of them. A gym conversation: "I don't see
why you bother," I'd venture, "women don't like packers.

48

They prefer – the *sensitive, affectionate* man." He: "With quads like that, you haven't got much else to offer, have you?" He knew it was cutting, had probably rehearsed it.)

We lived in Hel(l)sworth (delete as applicable), a grimy suburb a couple of miles beneath the western edge of the capital, at the blunt cutting edge of evolution. I say "beneath", because it's true. A few hundred years ago, exactly between the Great Fire of 1666?7? and the imminent Third World War (there's bound to be one if everyday guys like me do stuff like this), Helsworth sprung up, insidious and spiteful, bomb-shelter houses squat and uncompromising, like some whopping great metastasizing tumour. It lived under the city's jaundiced skin – dormant – until the first of the blacks moved in. Civil, soulful, underemployed, we had arrived. The town hated us, vilified us, yet we gave it life, and a swollen "underclass" to sit on. There we lay, under the capital, under the town, under the dole. Ever tried being under three bums at once? It's hot, and we were bothered.

I lived around the corner from Otieno, and that was at the central loop of the black community, which leaked gumbo as it snaked through the boroughs. We vigorously avoided the local hardcores, the Ragga-Muffins ("Remember," said Otieno, "behind those flashing gold fillings there are only ulcers and old *kwon*."), and craved American sport in every chemical form. "NBA Throughout The Day!" "Early In The Morning – Alonzo Mourning!" "Brad Faxon And Reggie Jackson!" We were good kids, weren't dossers. We did some weights at the gym under the disappointed gaze of the instructor, who evidently hoped we'd steal a few medicine balls (they were too damned *heavy* to lift! and what would we do with them?), trimmed the grass and came home at nine-thirty. But I ran from all this one day, from the blighted, overpriced mangoes, the three forty-two an hour at sterile KFC.

I wasn't feeling lazy one afternoon. My brother once called me lazy-as-hell, and I retorted that I didn't feel it, but that was plain stupid. If you're really lazy, you don't feel it. Laziness is special because you don't know it's there, it isn't normally accompanied by any sensation of activity; it's detectable only in its absence, like all the really pacifist elements that occur in nature. Otieno had come round. Today's topic of discussion was crime, how bad it was in the area, why, how everyone was defined by their misdeeds. We chatted at a canter – no, come to think of it, he did, since he enjoyed that, and I listened, oppressed by his heavy words. Trying to get him off one of his elegant speeches was like screwing balsa wood through metal. Occasionally, I'd burst out; but this was so rare that such speeches were known as The Greatest Hits.

"One day," he began, tall, emotive, African, "everyone on the planet will be guilty of something." He loved sweeping statements and the hand movements that came with them.

"That's ridiculous." I had gained the heat in this argument. "You suggest that guilt will be universal, that do-gooders will be the deviants of the future? And what of children?"

"Yes, even children." A *jwic*, harsh, prolonged. "Adults," he went on, "will be blamed for homicides, the decline of literature, tax evasion, most kids for not stopping them, except the really perceptive ones ('Mummy! Surely cigarettes aren't deductible!'). And babies, wet, pink, orange, black, for just being on the Earth, sucking out every last, dull, brown nitrogenous drop, draining our resources—"

"I'll give you this – you talk good trash. You've heard of HIV-positive kids, right? No – of course you have, you've heard of every damn thing there is to hear of. But that isn't blame, is it? You can't blame the kids, can you?"

"No – you misunderstand me. The promiscuous parents are to blame, with their amoral whoremones and their one-a-day policy. The ill-qualified doctors with the faulty syringes are to blame; the child is merely an envoy of the pain, the misfortunes and – *mistakes* – of the ancestors are visited unto future generations—"

"What about cocaine addicts in the womb, then? Do you just blame the drug? What about all that grainy white stuff, creeping in there, surfing on plasma, nuzzling in; cowardly, crystalline, clandestine; under thin webs of protein – jumping all over the soft little pulsing segment of Mum and crackhead partner, so all the weenie wants on World Entrance is a syringe. What next? Foetal felons? Pre-natal pimps? It's not as simple as all that.

"There are two theories. Some guys say that God moves in mysterious ways, others that the Universe is some kind of galactic casino (maybe they're the atheists; you're not one, are you?), that we're all different; the cosmos' only aim is to create an infinite range of diversity. That obviously needs some criminals, right?

"Me; I buy both of those, because I can see that happening all over the place. While we're watching the footy, sleeping in until 2pm, God moves—" I knew it was dodgy. Otieno was on to it.

"Yeah, very good. Put it all down to God, the one person we can't see. Are you going to carry on like this?"

"He rakes in the stellar chips, casting one here, first Otieno, then a 16-year old mother with triplets on the way, another there, a bustling junglist from Ealing Broadway via the Old Orleans Cafe and M25. Me; and the OAPs, shovels-full of them, living off processed peas, wishing they were back in the war. Me; here I was, five-ten, clean except the upper back (arrrrgh!) between the shoulder blades: I can't reach there, even with a loofah, place is like a no-fly zone for water, an enclave for rebel filth), eighteen. Standing erect, 170lb, grade C in abdominal strength, on the brink of alcohol and the vote. Oh, and Manchester. A BBB offer for Chemistry, to join the campus; the land of pretty tutors, Champions League football every fortnight, late nights, later nightclubs: the definitive, cosmopolitan, honesttoGod social fulcrum of the known Universe. And a few practicals, here and there, to fill in the time. To conclude: you've got other stuff that makes you different, not just sin, sin, sin, sin. I mean, I'm sure no one else sees Man. University like that. Some people might go there to do work, or Physics, I dunno." It was a valiant attempt, considering it was off the cuff (and mostly irrelevant), but Otieno knew he had won, and closed out with a slight misquote.

"I heard someone Greek say that emotions impair a man's judgement, that he is caught up 'in his own pleasure and pain'. Don't get involved in your debate." Aristotle – he always finished with Aristotle, it was the only stuff he read. The thing about quoting the dead great thinkers is that no one can argue with them; they're all dead, their words are accepted like law. Dry, exhausted, we lay back and quaffed our juice. That was the trick; if you were a waffling philosopher you didn't deal in pounds Sterling but in saliva; who could talk longest before dehydrating. Too much phlegm and you went vocally bankrupt.

Yeah, school; the best thing about the whole area. Helsworth Grammar, State, maintained. Five hundred students, blue blazers, ADT-sponsored, who all took the bright, clean alleyways home. Locals, Asians, GP's daughters, an MP's son, Africans and Jamaicans from about four different blackgrounds throughout London. We came from all over the place; a really eclectic? esoteric? mix. We sought straight "A"s and good university offers, equally as hard to come by. And the worst thing was that we all did really well, chased Hasmonean High in the exam league tables. Didn't lose anything except regional snooker, dodgy chalk anyway, unlike Swakeley's or the other local dumps. And at three-ten every weekday we lost it again and again. Smiling, peripheral, everyone diffused cheerfully to high and low corners of the metropolis, wafting away, fading scents. They abandoned us with the school grounds, buff, sandy, impersonal. We met the victim here, in these tidy yellow fields.

It's fine where I am, I've been absorbed into the high-pressure bloodrush of city life. It's easy to drop in and be assimilated, a breeze. I only needed a haircut and a little skin lotion. The landlord doesn't care about much except his rent, my new manager doesn't have time for concern: I'm just another hornet in a hive. Otieno's around, stunned, hovering over some crowded marketplace, invisible. Has he changed? I can't decide.

No, not that – why we did it. Why we took him down. I mean, the girl wanted help (obviously! you'll see later!), but she ran off, didn't she? After that it was just us and him, old, squat, lecherous. I mean, if we went to court the whole thing would just fall apart; she scarpered when he was brooding, intact: *still alive*. She wouldn't even recognise photos of him now (maybe she thinks it was a gangland killing! Absurd!). Murderers – what a bunch of cowards. They all say that at the time of the victim's death, their minds are blank, virgin-white, can't control themselves. They know exactly what they're thinking (own up, you guys!). We were disgusted. We did it. We knew.

We shouldn't have left the house.

We left the house at six-forty, basketballs, half-pressure, pounding up the hill beside us. I'd just washed; the bath burped, and the sky was a blue-rinse, as though it had been doused with cheap bleach. Our roundabout route to the courts cut a cross-section through the town, surgical. We crossed the Cromwell estate – "Into the Shadow of the Valley of the Full-time Skinheads," Otieno quipped – briskly, down from the loony fringe into the town centre. The area was boiling with Asian investment, bhangra music, wild, exotic, steamed in thick swathes from most of the shopfronts. I didn't have 2-quid-nineteen for a Whopper (A Whopper? I don't see much whop about it. It's about 120 grams of sugar, oil and beef, where from I don't know, hidden by a scabrous wad of bun. Who's going to pay that kind of money for a sloppy pancake of meat and gherkin? What happened to honest blue-collar market research?), so we passed through.

We descended towards the grammar, and through the torn fence caught sight of the netless hoops, about 400 metres distant. I tensed a calf muscle, oblong, curved, oblong, curved, and heard a whimper (was that my leg creaking?); stopped immediately, you shouldn't overdo this physical exertion thing. The whimper, recent, continued. We moved alongside the edge of the grass, towards a hazy green clearing. We saw him.

We saw her. She was thin, weak. The man had a big cold knife, sharp. It flashed down through the sun. It flashed down across her naked back. He laughed. She had a gag on her mouth, tight blue, wet; couldn't scream. He laughed again, I think he was carving up her back, writing his name, he'd got to S-E-B, had a hell of a long way to go yet, then what, his surname, maybe a few initials, *she* wasn't going to last that long—

Otieno turned away rudely, *unlike him*, towards the main complex. I followed him, silent, as we came to the scaffolding, and he tossed me a tube, a thick metal pipe. He turned brusquely, aggressive, and lifted me bodily out of his way. I crashed on my side; his eyes were solid, dull as teak, and the pipe was set in his hand. Then he began to run, manic, to the taller grass.

When I caught up the man had got to S-E-B-A and half of the S. He was old, vicious, his eyes were veined, violent. He held the knife like a dagger, his knee sunk in the small of her back. As he began the downward arc, his skin rolled through four shades of pink, something green bubbled under his thick veins, he was going to—

"Stop."

Where the hell had that come from?

Otieno exhaled, logical. The air turned colder around his mouth. The man turned around. I rushed over to the girl, pulled her away from the man and her bonds, let her scream. I was a little rough, she fell in the nettles, abused me as if she knew me, and scrammed; loped away into the bushes, with a medley of thin blood and steel shavings crawling down her back. The man knelt in the grass, dazed. Otieno raised his weapon, high and judgemental.

The bar, wrought iron, rich oxide-orange then dull red, came down *whishthud* on the front of his head, a little creaky in the backswing but it did the trick. His scalp exploded into a hot welt, the skin was wider on his skull. That did it for me.

We finished him off with a few more blows, I don't know how many more. Flailing wildly(me), arms like ebony hacksaws, poles cracking so hard, off-centre, straight (Otieno), firm, *tak, tak, tak*.

We left him crumpled in the light rough, with the bars, the knife, and went. Towards the station, change rustling through our long pockets. Above, the sky was raw, mimicking the Earth we fled with, casting down a warped reflection upon our villainous heads. Black clouds, grey pavement; rain in clouds, hail on soil.

We didn't speak on the train out, sat two carriages away from each other. I slept. Visions of home, the town, the man. The shock at school; murderers in their Sixth Form, done a runner. The semi-witness, the girl with the engraved back. I woke. Otieno was shuffling along the cold platform, jacket brown and ragged under the orange nightlights. I turned my head towards him, he saw me, grimaced, and threw his shirt over the sign, obscuring it, left it there until the train pulled out. I haven't seen him around.

Me? For crying out loud, assault convicts are *hard*, with mottled cheeks, raw nail-slashed cannonballs of muscle and a permanent supply of renewable black eyes. That's not my scene; I even used Johnson's baby shampoo ("No more tears!") once, as a toddler, but it wasn't much use on Afro hair. I don't walk with a real limp, don't burp extravagantly while eating out. My legs splay almost obtusely at the knees, and my knees? If I was at an American crossroads they'd point to First and Third. Flat feet. Not much good on the 100m track, only about thirteen-five-o. Not very archetypal, if you know what I mean.

And, to put that in context, there's a third theory I forgot to tell you about. Crime makes criminals of us all; if you think about it, it is, must be, the greatest Diversifier, sorts us all into classes. Forget State and public schools, Geordies and Scousers; you don't have to be cool, purple, Nordic and/or one-legged (though I guess it would help with balance) to take someone out with a shotgun. There are so many different types of sin, drunk-and-disorderly, GBH with intent, larceny (sounds great!), malfeasance, you can do anything you like with this infinite range. It's just like they make up names on purpose, just to make sure there aren't any kooky wiseguys and saintly Oxbridge graduates floating about above the law. They have a class system all of their own, first/second/third degree, and here we are, me and Otieno, inexplicably princes of the whole illicit, litigious, irreligious heap, killers on a sweat-drenched afternoon. And here I am, inexplicably, sitting on top of the dole, the town, and the capital.

Samantha Villard (8)

My Sister Franky

My sister Franky was embarrassing from the moment she was born. She had so much hair that my mum called her the gorilla. I thought she looked more like an eskimo baby. People said how pretty she was, but we knew they were just kidding.

When Franky was three months old, she started being sick over everything. She was sick over people, the floor, herself and the furniture. This seemed to last for ever.

When we used to take Franky out in the buggy, people used to stop and say hello to her, but she used to pull funny faces and poke her tongue out.

When we used to go shopping to Kingston, Franky's favourite trick was to take things from shops and hide them in her buggy. My mum had to take back to the shops – a shoe, a pair of sunglasses and some marbles. Once in a clothes shop, Franky was grumpy with my mum and she hid in the window pretending to be one of the models.

She's also embarrassing at home. A few times my mum and dad have had friends around, and Franky has come downstairs with a pair of knickers on her head. Sometimes when my friends come round for tea, Franky takes her clothes off at the dinner table.

Now that Franky can talk, she's even more embarrassing. She embarrasses me on the bus because she sings really loud, and she embarrasses my mum on the bus because she talks about "How do babies get into mummies' tummies, and why don't daddies have babies?"

Last week when my mum came home from Kingston she said "Franky has really embarrassed me in Monsoon" (a clothes shop). Mum was trying on a dress and Franky came running out of the changing rooms and shouted, "Mummy's in the changing rooms with no clothes on and she's all fat and wobbly." Everyone in the shop laughed.

But when she cuddles up to me on the sofa and says "I love you, Sam", I wouldn't swap her for any other sister.

P.S. Franky starts school in September. I wonder who's going to be the lucky teacher!

Isla Guild (12)

Clouds

The hot sun shines on my face and I feel its warmth. I am lying on my back, watching the clouds pass overhead. If I stare at them for long enough, they turn into shapes – my cat Rocky, a star, a bicycle . . . a twisted bicycle . . . I prop myself up on my elbows and look to the other end of the garden. Mummy and Daddy are sitting at the picnic table, laughing. I don't know what they are laughing at but it doesn't matter. They are laughing.

Rocky trots up to me and I stroke him. His fur is warm. He is still only a kitten, very small, but Mhairi says he will grow bigger. Daddy says he'd better, because we bought him to catch mice. Daddy doesn't like mice. Mhairi says it's because they're small and they run about. Rocky spreads himself on my stomach and we lie in the sun, me stroking him and him purring loudly. We are happy. Rocky is very happy. He hasn't seen Mhairi for a long time but he will this afternoon.

I close my eyes and listen to him purr. In my mind I see a motorbike . . . I open my eyes. I don't want to think about this. But I can't stop myself and my mind is like a camera showing pictures, some in order, some not. I have no control over the camera and I remember. I remember it all . . .

I am eating my cereal and watching morning TV. I am thinking about how I would like to hit Timmy Mallet over the head with his pink mallet. Daddy is checking his briefcase in the hall. When he moves I can hear loose change and keys jingling in his pockets. The front door opens and Danielle runs in, panting. She wants to know where

Mummy is. I tell her. Timmy hits a girl over the head with his mallet and I throw my spoon at the TV. Mum comes thundering down the stairs and the next thing I know I am in the car. Daddy is driving fast and I am thinking he must be very late for work.

We stop at the Blind Corner and they jump out of the car. Daddy's tie flies over his shoulder and I tell him but he isn't listening. They are running towards a blanket in the middle of the road. It is not a very nice blanket and I am wondering why anyone would want it. I am thinking perhaps that is why they threw it into the road. I wouldn't want a bright red blanket. But I see there is something under the blanket. I hear a siren in the distance and suddenly think maybe I don't want to look under the blanket. I sit down on the kerb and watch people gather round the blanket. I put my head in my lap and wait for them to come and see what is wrong. I wait.

I look up. They haven't noticed me sitting on the kerb. The ambulance is here and two men are lifting the blanket inside. Suddenly everyone is gone. The ambulance, the crowd, all gone, and I am left on the kerb alone. There is a woman standing over me. She tells me to go into her house but I know I'm not supposed to talk to strangers. So I say no thank you, politely. But she takes my hand anyway and soon I am sitting on a brown couch. The pattern is swirly and I trace it with my fingers. A man smiles at me and asks me if I want a biscuit, so I say yes. Soon the phone rings. The lady answers it and listens. She tells me it's Mummy. I want to talk to her but she is already gone.

I stay with the people for a long time. When we are out in the garden and I am lying on a sunbed, the man goes away and comes back with Daddy. I am very happy to see him. We get in the car and start to drive home. Only we are not going home, we are going in the other direction and we are in the car for a long time.

We stop outside a big red building. There is a sign on the gate but the words are too long for me to read. I think one of them is "Norwich". Inside the building the corridors are clean and shiny and the smell is not one I know. It smells . . . clean. There is a big clown on the wall and we go past a fishtank. I want to stop and look at the fish but Daddy won't let me. So we carry on walking.

I see people in beds. I smile at them but they don't smile back. They don't look very happy. I see Mummy at the end of the corridor, talking to a nurse. I know it is a nurse because I have a matching uniform at home. Me and Mhairi play doctors and nurses. I usually have to be the patient but I don't mind. The nurse smiles at me and I am glad someone seems happy. The nurse shows me her watch, which is attached to her shoulder. I have one on my uniform but it's not real.

Mummy and Daddy are sitting next to a bed. I don't want to look at the bed but they are beckoning so I go. Mhairi doesn't look happy either. I can see why. Her leg is stuck in the air and I wonder how it stays there. Her hair is dirty and I wonder why she doesn't wash it. I don't want to look at her face. It is covered with red scratches. I want to cheer her up but I don't know how. There isn't another chair so I sit on the next bed. I don't want to hear what they are saying.

Over the next six weeks we visit the building twice a day. I don't really mind. I like the playroom and I like looking at the walls . . . When I get there I want to go to the play room but Mummy and Daddy want me to sit with them. I can't please everyone. Mhairi has had the contents of her room transferred to her bed and now posters and cuddly toys are all round her. Her bed has a ceiling because she needs something to hang her leg off, so most of her posters hang from that.

At school, everyone wants to know how Mhairi is. Really, I think everybody's over-reacting about it, even Mummy and Daddy. That's what I tell them, anyway. But I'm not sure. The doctors always smile at me and look happy and sound happy, but how do I know if they're telling the truth about Mhairi? If they can put on such an act of cheerfulness, surely they could just as easily lie about her? If Mhairi was going to be all right, she wouldn't be in that bed. Mum's crying all the time – she wouldn't be doing that if everything was OK. And Dad doesn't say anything. Maybe he doesn't want me to know. If people at school thought she was all right, they wouldn't be asking about her all the time, would they? How do I know she is if no one will tell me? I may be only seven, but I can take it. No matter what happens, I'd much rather know about it. But no one will tell me . . .

Mhairi is crying. I don't want to look at the place in her leg where the pin just came out. The nurses try to cover it up but I can see it. Daddy tells me not to look. But it's all right, the nurses are closing the door. Mum looks scared. I know something's the matter. The smell gets to me again. It's so clean, and that, mixed with the polish on the floors, is starting to give me a headache. Daddy doesn't seem upset, he's reading a newspaper, and he has a teddy under his arm to give to Mhairi. I like the teddy. It's got nice eyes.

When Mhairi comes out an hour later, I'm nearly asleep. They wheel her bed down the corridor. I can hear the wheels squeaking on the polished floor but I'm too sleepy to open my eyes . . .

I snap my eyes open. Rocky opens his and jumps off my stomach. I look up at the clouds but the shapes are gone.

I settle on my back again and stare hard at the clouds. I wonder what Mhairi is doing at this moment. She doesn't want to leave the hospital now, but Mummy and Daddy say she has to. She's got crutches because her leg's in plaster. I wanted to play on them but they're too big for me.

Mhairi says the scar on her chin will heal up but her leg will take a little longer. Her femur is broken. I'm not sure what it is but it's something to do with her thigh. Everybody still wants to know how she is. I wish they wouldn't ask.

Daddy has gone to pick her up in the car. Mummy's making lunch. And me and Rocky are in the garden. I know Rocky's happy Mhairi is coming home. And so am I. (But don't tell her I said that.)

Katie Bishop (6)

Tooth down the Plughole

When my wobbly tooth fell out
It went down the plughole
And I thought that it was lost.
But I didn't cry.
My sister said, "Now the tooth fairy won't come."
And she gave me 10p
To make up for it.

But Mummy undid the pipe
And we found it
Looking sad and wet
In the U bend.
Then I was happy.

Gemma McKean (12)

Frances Stevens (17)

Luke Harney (14)

*SKY

A single shout of panic and an almost blinding white light sped towards them. Positions were hurriedly taken, then all hell broke loose.

The train was upon him. The heavy wheels grating against the rusted rails jostled and jolted the sleepers either side of him in their fixings. The whining brakes mingled with the staccato clatter of metal against metal, seeming to shake the very fabric of reality around him. Blood rushed to his ears and very soon a new sound was added to the discord. His screams of absolute terror, loud at first, then fading only to be lost to the chaos.

James packed his battered record bag with his paints. Some blues; a white for highlights; an aqua marine; a red, a yellow and an orange for his tag; four cans of black. A record played on his turntables and he moved as he packed, head nodding to the slow, languid sub-bass which emanated from a single, floor-standing speaker. Beats weaved a rhythmic, pounding dance through the fluid waves of a string instrumental and were joined by another cross-rhythm, skilfully scratched in by the DJ. James hated having to turn off his stereo in the middle of a track: somehow interrupting the music before it reached its natural conclusion seemed to leave him feeling mixed up inside. It was as if a surgeon had got inside him, messed around a bit and then sewed him back up, without putting things back in place first. He had a bit of an obsession for hearing music exactly as the artist meant it to be heard and only having one speaker was already seriously compromising his high standards. Today, however, James was going to a place he had never been to before and he didn't have much time to get there. A packet of crisps and his personal stereo went into the bag and with a wince he stopped the record in time.

The volume increased. Terrified that an odd piece of metal might be hanging down from the underside of the train he desperately tried to shrink back into the hard ground. Not daring to turn his head either way for fear of it being knocked off, he stared straight ahead, eyes wide open. He had not imagined it would be like this. No lucid scenes from his past flashed before his eyes and no thoughts of friends or family entered his mind. Only the insistent clamour of the train's under-carriage on his ears seemed to permeate into every molecule of his being. Without noticing it he had stopped screaming. His mouth was wide open, but no sound came out.

Slamming the door behind him as he left, James cursed as the door stuck and he had to wrench it to get the latch to click on the inside. He pulled on his worn-out pair of flat-soles and slung his bag over one arm and his head. As he pulled the porch door closed James stopped to adjust the strap in the old green-tint glass which was at one time on every front door on the road. Now most had been replaced by clear glass or had been smashed by drunks on their way back from the White Lion. Satisfied with his appearance he stepped over the old tabby, stretched out in the midday sun, and began walking down the road in the direction of Acton Yard.

How long could this train be? Seconds stretched and morphed into minutes and the noise did not stop.

Acton Yard. The graffiti hall of fame. The place where only the bravest had their tags. A place where the art-form was only viewed by fellow artists and not by the eyes of the public, a public who view art as being in galleries, not all around them. James could not stand it when teachers lectured him on the likes of David Hockney and how their art related so well to the world around him. He did not have anything against Hockney in particular, but teachers could never understand James' fascination with the three letters which spelt his tag. They were always finding new ways to discourage him. Usually by citing a "great" artist's work and trying to point out ways in which James' art form was so inferior. SKY. That was what he wrote. The S and the K were his mother's initials, but James never told anybody that. Although not necessary in street art the Y made it into a real word and James often thought of it as being a symbol. The missing part which would have made his mother the woman she never was. Teachers could not understand how three letters painted in different ways could ever convey as much emotion as a Picasso or a Van Gogh, but James knew. His art was not for sale, he donated it to the world. A chunk of real-life for commuters as they sat in packed trains at Victoria station, a small amount of real emotion for the crack-heads and dopeys crouched in subways around London, an item of real art for only a few.

Without reason or prompting a single image forced its way through the barricade of noise and into James' head. His mother. His mother as if transfigured, hands clasped serenely at her waist, looking into his eyes. It was an image far removed from James' one living memory of her:

The scene is black and white. Images blur and re-focus at odd times. Movements leave white trace-marks on the vision. The door swings open in front of you. It is the door to the living room. In the far corner there is a figure sprawled on a chair. The chair is old and yellow, there are rips in it. On a nearby table there is an ashtray and some heroin syringes. You know this because you've seen them before. The figure groans. The image fades.

She seemed far more relaxed than she had ever been when she was alive and the expression she wore was one of completeness. As though she knew. Then the darkness enveloped him like a shroud.

When he arrived at Acton Yard, only a short tube ride from his gran's house, Tom was already there, cheap cigarette hanging from one corner of his mouth. Tom was a friend, not a good friend, more of an acquaintance. The greetings were short and to the point and in a couple of minutes they were on platform four, looking as casual as possible. Although not packed, the platform was still buzzing with people. The two agreed that they would wait until the next train had come and gone before descending, so as to avoid the risk of being spotted. Time passed and the train arrived, taking most of the people with it. Only a few remained: a crusty, some students and a subway official. It was a simple matter for Tom to grab the man's hat, run round the dividing block and leave the hat on the other side before returning and following James down from the platform in-between the rails. Out of breath from their run, they walked in the direction of where the train had come from, towards the yard. The tunnel was dark and Tom flicked on a pocket torch to light the way. When they reached the spot, they knew. A single halogen bulb lit a rough-hewn area of soot black stone and what covered the walls took their breath away. Metre after metre of the most eclectic blend of graffiti you can imagine. Abstract letters, words, pictures. James recognised a couple of the tags, some of his hip-hop mates had done Acton a few months ago. With sweaty hands he undid the Velcro of his bag, took out a can and made the first incision.

The blackness exploded into a plume of colour. As he opened his eyes, James was greeted by the iridescent, yellow glow of a dirty lamp. His ears throbbed with pain and his mouth was dry. From up ahead a whoop of triumph sounded. Tom was jumping up and down, enthusing about "a rush". James turned away, ashamed of his friend. As though she knew. The words floated into his head. He had seen her and he knew what he must do. Wordlessly he picked up his paints and finished the tag. It was a giant piece, surrounded by a roving white border seeming to shimmer on the wall. It was his best. James stood back and looked at it. Knowing in his heart he would never write those three letters again.

Sabbinah Alabas (10)

Leila Hobday (6)

I'm Too Ill

I don't want to do this
I don't want to do that
I'm too ill, I'm too ill.
Its PE today, I can't go to
School I'm too ill, I'm too ill.
My teeth are all itching
And my hair hurts
My belly is wobbly
And my eyes twirl round.
I'm too ill, I'm too ill.

Oh it's art today
I'll go anyway!

Mali Dray (16)

She's Wearing your Hat

She's wearing your hat
The one you tried on in the window
You posed and pretended to be a mannequin
I said yeah, you do look like a dummy
You laughed and hit me
You didn't buy it.
She's wearing your hat
The one that sat on your hair
Like a ladybug
Until the assistant showed you how to turn up the brim
She said it suited the shape of your face
You almost bought it.
She's wearing your hat
The one that was still there last week
(I happened to be passing)
The mannequin who wore it
It didn't suit the shape of her face
You should have bought it.
She's wearing your hat
The one that looked so good on you
(I didn't tell you)
The one I wanted you to buy
(I didn't tell you)
The one we said would never sell
(We laughed)
You said who would want a hat
That looked like a bug?
She's wearing your hat.

CANDLE ON THE WATER

Janice Pinfold (17)

Louise Bralsford (6)

I will be your Candle on the Water

I will not be your flower,
I will not be a piece of your heart,
I will be exactly what I am from the start.

I will not be your son,
I will not be your daughter,
All I want to be is your candle on the water.

When I am your candle on the water I don't want a boat,
All I want to do is float,
And as I float silently away from the shore,
You will only see me for seconds then I will be no more.

I will not be your son,
I will not be your daughter,
All I want to be is your candle on the water,
Candle on the water,
Candle on the water.

Katherine McGrath (16)

Chocolat with Charlot

He was there again, in the same place as always, standing very still. His little bowler perched on top of a small face made up a startling white, apart from black eyebrows and a little black moustache. His short grubby jacket did not reach his wrists and his bare ankles stuck out of the cheap, black trousers. The huge boots and the little cane completed the picture of Charlot, still as his counterpart in Madame Tussaud's, on the corner of the Place Saint-Germain. A sad little crowd paused to watch, standing away from him as if held back by an invisible barrier. A small child tugged at his mother's coat and whispered:

"Pourquoi reste-il toujours comme ça, Maman?" The mother moved on, feeling the cold of the February evening, and pulled him along with her.

The rest of the crowd stood bemused and waited idly for the figure to come to life and entertain them. Up the steps from the metro came a sudden rush of passengers who swept through the crowd and passed the still figure like the flurries of snow that blew down the cold streets. Only a girl stopped, as she always did. She hesitated a moment, smiling to herself, then as Charlot showed no sign of performing, she started to move towards her apartment, happy at the thought that she would soon be warm and out of the snow, at home. She had only taken a few steps when ragged applause broke out from the attentive audience. She turned back to see what was happening.

Charlot had sprung into life and was entertaining the crowd with his funny walk and his smiling face. When Charlot noticed that she had turned to look, he went into an elaborate routine. He became very coy and bashful,

Sarah Lacey (17)

Lucy Daynes (17)

twirled his stick, put his knees together and shook his body with delight, and looked at her with huge brown eyes. The crowd turned to look, to see who he was falling in love with.

As the traffic on the Boulevard Saint-Germain sped away from the lights, he took the flower from his lapel and offered it to her. He went down on one knee in the snow and beseeched her to take it. When she stepped forward and accepted it, he smiled with the biggest smile she had ever seen and shuffled away from her, both feet stuck out, and making little joyful bounces every few steps. He turned, smiled at the audience, blew kisses, waved his hat, took a long, dramatic bow and watched sadly as they drifted away through the slush leaving no more than a few francs.

She too had moved away, feeling the dry cold in her cheeks and still thinking of home. She turned back once more to find those dark eyes fixed on her. He was looking at her with a terrible intensity. Was this still Charlot or was there someone else looking out through the mask? The world still rushed past oblivious. His thin fingers tipped his hat forward as he bent almost imperceptibly from the waist. She felt compelled to stand looking at him. He stretched out a thin finger towards her, then moved his two fingers like a pair of legs walking, then pointed to himself and to her and offered an arm for her to take.

She laughed. He shuffled over to her, and she put her arm through his. He stopped and somebody, Charlot or the man inside the mask, was smiling at her with a different kind of gratitude. She shivered, perhaps with the cold. He pointed to the café across the Place, Les Deux Magots. She nodded, and wondered why she had agreed so readily to taking a coffee with an unknown young man.

Inside the crowded café, he showed her to an empty table. They sat side by side. She turned and wanted to say something to him but could not find any words. She noticed the grey bags under his eyes through the thick white make-up. When the waiter came with the menu, she put her finger on "Chocolat". The waiter nodded and looked at Charlot. He put his finger on top of hers.

"Alors, deux chocolats. C'est tout?"

Neither replied; they were both looking at their fingers touching. The waiter took the menu away and their hands fell apart. The waiter looked at the girl with an amused quizzical smile. It was true they were an odd couple.

Though neither spoke, or because neither spoke, they felt comfortable with each other. His face remained both Chaplin and the young man inside the mask. He had stopped playing the clown and began to look very young and vulnerable.

The chocolat arrived and they drank it together, grateful for its smooth warmth. Still not a word between them. She saw the dark, thick sediment revealed and wished that the cup would never be empty. She had no desire to go out in the cold and finish this dreamlike encounter with Charlie Chaplin in the Deux Magots.

Charlot looked up and saw something or somebody outside. The girl looked to see who or what it was.

Peering in through the window, was Columbine – a young woman in traditional Commedia dell'Arte costume and make-up – looking angrily at Charlot. He got up from the table, frowning and anxious, then turned and gave her a wonderful display of charming and sad farewell and left the restaurant. As she watched them going off together, she could see their animated conversation. Charlot was talking.

The waiter arrived and presented her with the bill. He smiled at her. She smiled back; for once she was happy to pay.

Nicola Elliott (10)

Shona Ferguson (15)

Alarm Clock (a Love Poem)

We compared alarm clocks.
Yours was shiny, clean and new;
mine was old, but in good condition
for its age.
"Doesn't matter," you said.

Your clock said a quarter to midnight;
mine said two o'clock in the afternoon,
and I wanted it to stay that way.
"Wind it forward," you said,
but I didn't want to.

Your clock's hands moved quickly;
my clock's minutes seemed to wander along
trying to turn themselves into hours.
"It needs a new battery," you said,
but I liked watching the hands move slowly.

Your clock was getting on for midnight,
and soon the alarm went off.
"Is that the time already?" you said.
"I must be off." You left.
You forgot to take your clock.

Your clock started a new day;
my clock stopped.

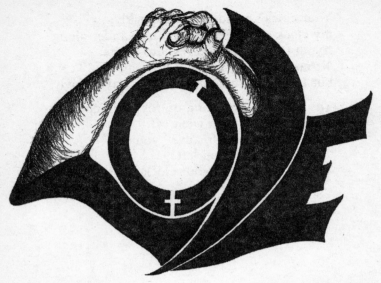

Amy Cooper (16)

Jessie Errey (15)

*In Check

In most game situations, an invaluable part of the action is the Queen, which has few conventions of movement unlike the other pieces. The Queen can move in any direction for an unspecified distance or number of squares without stopping until she reaches an obstacle or a boundary.

The pawn, although a vital piece in the game, has restricted movement; the pawn can only move one square at a time, with an exception at the beginning of the game, where it can move two squares forward. The pawn is the

*only piece which cannot retreat back into its own side,
but has to continue towards the opponent...*

Taken from *Chess for Beginners*

"Check," I said. My pawn – Francie called them prawns
– and my knight were threatening Francie's king. The
hapless king sat stolidly in grave unmoving jeopardy, chip-
crowned. "It's broken," I remarked unnecessarily. "It's
wearing a jester hat."

"Oh, for God's sake," Francie said, scattering the chess
pieces. Unharvested, they would lie there for some time.
Maybe even forever – a Francie-forever – which might be
a day, a week, a month, mildewing in the grass. My white
bishop had fallen next to Francie's knight. It looked
grubby nestling against the smooth mahogany. Francie
always plays black. Black always wins, Francie often tells
me. It even says so in *Good Housekeeping*. "Come on,"
she cried, her voice ripe with possibilities.

"Hey!" I said pointlessly, playing for time. "Just because
you were losing."

"That was a contributing factor," replied Francie airily.
Her cloudy soda eyes flickered with impatience. "Come
on!" she repeated.

"God, look at your eyes," I said, staring at her, legi-
timately now. "You look like you've got three minutes to
live and want to get it over with."

"I can't look at my eyes," she returned, irritated. "Can
you look at yours?"

"Yes, with a mirror," I replied, and immediately
regretted it. What a stupid thing to say; the laws of science
don't seem to apply to Francie somehow, although she
pleads normality while dancing through the crowds.
Francie told me once she had a pair of secret wings, and
I never quite doubted her. "What do you want to do
instead?"

85

"Play duets on the pi," Francie said, and darted through the French windows. I heard her run upstairs; I listened, waiting for her to come back for me. I heard her playing a Chopin waltz. Pale butterflies lingered in the air like kisses.

The open-mouthed box silently pleaded me. "Francie," I called after her, "shouldn't we put them away . . .?" But the words sounded useless and pointless. I knew it, and she knew that, as long as she had me to keep on pleading her, begging her back with banalities and statistics, she could just keep on running and never look back. Maybe one day Francie would pull the rope up to which I had been clinging. One of us had to keep their feet on the ground, and although I knew Francie was up there in the stars calling my name, I despaired of trying to reach her. Jumping Jack Flash would get to her first; some gold-hatted, high-bouncing lover who never bothered with the practicalities.

Francie was playing the top half of Heart and Soul in the piano room. She can only play the top half of everything. Sometimes I like to think that she is incomplete without my part, that we are two interlocking puzzle pieces, but it's all a fantasy from a long time ago. I guess I will always need her more than she needs me. Or maybe we would die without one another; perhaps it's like a constellation, interdependent, transcending everything, an infinite pattern in the labyrinth of our lives. If one star dies, the constellation changes completely and metamorphoses into something new. But that's just Astronomy. Physics. Francie and me, I can't explain it scientifically. I have looked for love in the pages of textbooks with my heart like a bunsen burner and my soul like a crucible. Chemistry stared at me blankly; Science proved me wrong.

Loving Francie is like being in check – an infinite revolving circle where there is always the risk of going over the edge, out of your depth. This ethereal Francie is already out of my depth. I can't catch galaxies and net them into words the way she can. I always find a hole in my net from the spiked points of stars. I can't share Francie's dreams of diving into underground caverns and eating green apples on redbrick walls, because I'm scared that maybe I won't be able to live Francie's life of dreams and water-breathing moonlit gardens as effortlessly as she. I am prone to stomach ache and colds. Green apples give me diarrhoea. Francie makes them into people, with their arms of matchsticks and their shoes of plasticine. I don't know how well I know her. Sometimes her mind seems to go on forever and other times I feel that even I could write her character sketch. And sometimes, when we sit together and she tells me that she wants to play badminton in a large garden with cats and ghosts and forgotten things in all corners, it seems that the stars are nearly in my reach. And when she laughs, they seem so close that for a moment I could reach out and catch one, but I'm always too afraid to take my hand out of my pocket and put it round Francie's pale shoulders in case it goes right through and I find myself alone; I discover that this singing angel was never anything but an optical illusion.

A shaft of sunlight has come through Francie's French windows and is reclining across the ceiling. Someday, Francie might love me. Someday I will hold one of her stars in my hand and she will smile. Someday she might pull me up into her night sky, or let down her hair, Rapunzel-wise, for me to climb. Then it would be check-mate, and she would have won.

Francie is still playing Heart and Soul. She never gets tired of it. Francie has left the door of the piano room open and through it I can see her in her pansy dress, reds and blues and purples burning in the afternoon sun. Slowly I enter, cautious like an android, watching her fingers gliding across the keys. I am suppressing a desire to run into the sunlight, to penetrate the magic world that might be hiding in the blindness. I approach the piano. I begin to play, seeing only the black and white beneath my hands; we are both blind things here, united in our senselessness. My fingers stumble along the monochrome staircase, sliding across staves and octaves, white to black like a chessboard. The two rhythms merge.

Francie laughs and unexpectedly finishes the piece. We stand there silent for a split-second in the sun and in this burning shadow it seems, with our silhouetted forms, that she is the queen and I am the pawn.

"God, look at your eyes," Francie says. "You look like that broken chess piece."

"But the king doesn't have eyes. Just a hat."

"Like me," replies Francie cryptically. "I am a king with a broken crown."

"And I'm a king with no eyes," I say, smiling again.

"I'm a prawn."

"I'm a shrimp."

Francie laughs. I don't. It's a bad joke. "Guess what I am?" she says. "I'm an archangel. Francie the archangel. See my halo." She draws one around her head. I pretend to grab it and throw it out of the window like an aerobie. I look out into the gold. Perhaps the halo has burst and its light spread around the world.

"If you're a king with no crown, and I'm a king with no eyes, why don't we both play black together?"

"No. Black's best." Francie looks serious, suddenly.

I hold out my arm to Francie, half-joking, half-hoping. "Care for a walk, Monarch?"

"Naturally, my squire."

We walk to the window like old lovers. The afternoon sky is going down gracefully and the gilt-edged clouds are like Japanese tissue paper. Francie sits on the sill, which is dangerous, and I follow, wishing for a smile. Francie looks at me; she is happy. Venus blinks in the sky.

"If, at an advanced stage in the game, a pawn manages to reach the furthermost row of the opponent's side, it can be exchanged for one of the more valuable pieces that may have already been claimed."

I still have the picture – us in fancy dress; me with a solemn smile and dark glasses, Francie laughing with flashing blue eyes and a jester hat with a tuck in the cotton. One serious in black and the other grinning in white. "Well, look what you did," she had told me, happy-eyed. "You won the game." And we had both laughed into the night.

Now I am listening to Francie play a piece by Bach. I can accompany her on the violin. In the morning we played chess again – Francie playing black of course – but we had to stop because my black pieces and hers became tangled in the net of squares and we could no longer tell them apart.

The moon is shining outside like a dirty silver plate. Francie once said she had seen seventy pleiades sisters instead of just six. One day I'll have to check that on my telescope. Not now.

I have one of Francie's stars – a gold one off her costume – and she has one of mine. We swapped at the parade. Crumpled paper cosmos with blunted points. Somewhere dark and cerebral, I have my own silver galaxy, and Francie has a little part of it. One day the galaxies will merge, gold and silver, boy and girl, black and white. These days we are both winning at chess. We don't think alike, Francie and I. I dream of diving with Francie into black holes and our faces lit from underneath by candles. Francie doesn't understand my dreams, nor I hers. As I said, the laws of Physics don't seem to apply to Francie. I don't know if she could plummet endlessly down a black hole without touching the walls or hitting the bottom. But one of us has to keep our feet on the ground.

Ben Womack (12)

*To Those Who Die

I

One day he decided,
That it was over,
Enough was enough,
As the phrase says.

He'd never cared much for phrases, the clichés,
And had always preferred to walk out,
Across the pitch, with a bat and ball,
And throw the ball high,
High into the heavens,
So the dust on it was thrown off and sparkled like stars,
Then he would swing,
And the stars would be flung aside as the white, stitched
    planet hurtled across the grounds,
And fell, like a comet, on to the earth,
Far away, across the green grass.

Sadly today then, he picked up the white ball,
And hurled it into the air.
But today, it caught a tree branch,
And sprung back,
Collapsing on the bonnet of a car,
Setting off an alarm,
Which he hardly heard,
As he walked.

He remembered the crowds,
The cheers,
The beauty of the brown brown bat,
The green green grass
And the white white ball.

He remembered the pitchers,
The slow ones, the fast ones,
The ones who had a glint in their eye and then . . .
Hit, then run, run, run,
A score.

He glanced at his crippled legs now,
And sighed as he put his bat in his boot.
He was sad now, he thought,
Because back then, they always said,
That he was untouchable,
An immortal player.
Yet what was he now?
He wondered as he slipped into his car,
And let the deadly steam slowly rise,
As if it had been waiting in his car every day,
For this hour,
He did not think any more,
He slept.

II

He slipped unnoticed by the water's edge
As if he was a part of the place nature was used to
     greeting.
He swam out into the middle of the river,
Even though his body wouldn't let him,
It was a romantic end.
But if a man were to stop him in the street and ask him,
"Are you the man that was on that show?"
Or
"Are you that guy who was on that thing on TV?"
He would have to shake his head, replying,
"No, I wasn't there. I've never been on TV."
Maybe, in the closing, tiny whimper at the end,
There is a longing that this conversation will evolve,
That the other will ask something more.
Then the man will be able to say,
"Yes, I am a somebody,
I am one of the world's greatest somebodies.
If the word somebody was a God, I would be
     worshipped."
It is not, however, and the conversation seldom evolves
     more,
Than the other's apologetic cough,
And the man giving a small sigh.

Harriet Creed (14)

Rachael Canter (12)

Forever

If you cry whilst reading this,
Promise me you cry for happiness,
I'm right beside you,
Picking you up when you fall
And lifting you high if you fail.
I'll unthread your mistakes,
And weave together our happy thoughts for each day.

I'm laughing at your jokes and
Remembering the memories we made,
So please don't forget them.
I'm listening to your words,
And answering back in my silent way,
You'll see.

Do not change your expression when you say my name,
Move the same way if you smell my scent,
Melt your sadness into the shadows,
Laugh twice as loud
And sing a whole lot stronger,
For now you have two hearts to fill.

I'm always with you
Even when you feel alone.
We're both watching the same sun
And I'm here whenever you read this,
Forever.

Rose Beauchamp (16)

*Camomile Tea

When she dies,
they will pull back the carpet to find
a glitter of mirrors and pearls,
saffron and photographs
in silver frames and sepia,
her young smile and a faded cushion.
Orangeblossom and roses, the hearing she'd been losing,
a Christmas card. The scent of the rain in summer '23,
silk stockings and the dream of amethysts.
A list of forgotten things, a description
of the taste of the pull of the moon on the sea.
The other cufflink.
Dust of eighty years, her last kiss, the air she died in.

It will be one of those silent, chilly days. Carelessly,
they will let time in
through the paused window.

Laura Keynes (16)

*Streets of Soul

On my very first day at college, in my first English lesson, the teacher handed out a sheet of poems and asked:

"How does the structure of these poems affect their meaning?"

I looked down at the sheet and saw that each poem had a different shape. Only one of the poems really caught my eye. It was called "Pulsion" and the poet had written it after seeing a man play percussion in concert. The words had no formal arrangement but were spread over the page. I blurred my eyes and looked at it so the words wouldn't be there and all I'd see was the overall shape. Gradually it seemed to me that the words were arranged to make them look as though they were floating up, spreading out near the top of the page. Immediately a familiar image came into my head. I must have seen it in a film once or maybe a photograph, otherwise I can't explain why I'm carrying around such a strong image in my head.

Picture this: a black man standing way up high on top of a skyscraper, his white shirt flapping out behind him leaving his chest exposed to the wind. Around his neck hangs a saxophone on a black cord. He leant back, putting all his soul into his saxophone and playing out all his grief so it floated away into the sharp blue sky. He played like now was the only moment he had, up there with those white shirt tails flying, the sweat glistening on his forehead and the gold saxophone glinting under the near sun. I could see all his pain mingling with the notes coming out of that golden instrument and floating up into the sky, gradually separating and getting caught in the mesh of air.

I brought my eyes back to focus when I heard the

97

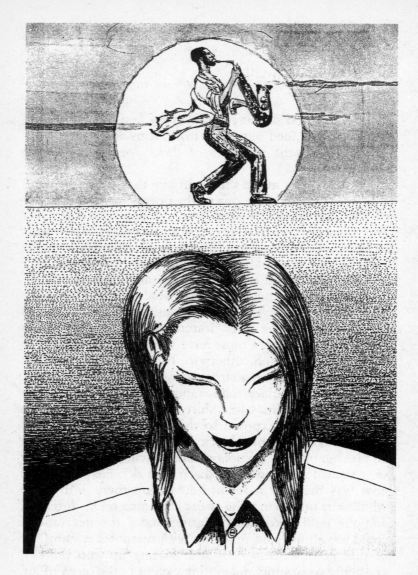

David Martin (17)

teacher asking me to explain the poem. She didn't know my name yet so she called me "the girl with the pink shirt on".

"Could the girl with the pink shirt on explain it to us?"

The girl with the pink shirt on panicked for a second and wondered how she was going to explain it to a room full of complete strangers.

"Well it's like a man playing a saxophone . . ." I started.

"The man in the poem's playing percussion," interrupted the teacher.

"I know, but if you blur your eyes a bit and . . ." I became aware of how stupid I sounded, and of how my face was clashing with my shirt. I heard the rustle of clothes as all the strangers adjusted their positions so they could gain a better view of my panic. Long silence.

"No, just forget it. Forget I said anything."

"What about you with the 'Dallas' T-shirt?"

The attention shifted to the stranger who had obviously bought his T-shirt at Dallas airport on a family holiday. Despite wanting to see the shirt I kept my head down, praying that they had forgotten.

I could see him so clearly; spine arched, black jeans, white shirt, fingers gliding and soul playing, but it was still hard to explain. Don't get me wrong, it wasn't so much the image I couldn't explain but how the black man's emotions were involved. It was the music that spread his emotions out, making them clear to him as they are to me. I wanted so much to share that man's release of energy and raw emotion so the rest of the English class would know what the poet saw when she watched a man play percussion in a concert. It is such a beautiful picture you can't just keep it to yourself. I still haven't tried to explain that poem to any of my friends.

I don't know how I got that image. Maybe I dreamt it or saw it on the cover of a record. Either way I think a little bit of me wants to be that person – standing there, knowing exactly who you are for just a moment and being able to say "This is what my life is about at this point in time." Imagine how it must feel; all alone, standing out against the sky in black and white Technicolor while the rest of the world lives below in the streets. I forgot to mention the streets, I spent too much time focusing the camera on the skyline. Down there it's dark and shadowy. If anyone's playing a saxophone he'll be doing it because he needs the money and he's sure to be blind and so old he can't arch his spine. His sax will have lost the bold glint it had in the days when the blind man played it on street corners with his friends just after the war had ended. Perhaps his ears work better than his eyes and he can pick out the strain of a young man's saxophone raining softly down to remind him of his own life and who he was.

Drug pushers live down there with pimps and the women who sell themselves, and the men that buy them. All the plastic bag people go by watching a world that thinks they're crazy. The plastic bag people know they're not crazy. They had the impulse to look up and they saw a man who knows exactly who he is too.

Perhaps I have the image because I want to forget what's down there in the street. I want to float into the sky like a little strain of music, high above all the others.

Jessie Errey (15)

*Watching Mr Adolescent

Flattened by his gaze
And pressed seductively, if involuntarily
Against a wall of static cling,
I watch his interest fluctuate
Like blips of electricity on a heart-rate monitor.
          Restraint cracking beneath an unfair code,
He wallows before me in pools of glutinous satisfaction
Blows floppy kisses through the gagging atmosphere
And swallows my dirty talk like a frog catching flies
      I sit across from him in a three mile wide tête-à-tête
Licking up his sagging declarations of love
As he belches promises at me
Drooling lustfully from all orifices;
I apply lipstick.
With sleepy urgency he begs for more
But my bleeding appliance has run rebelliously down my
    chin
And all at once I am a statuesque B-movie virgin
Teetering on a pedestal in greasy heels;
      I slip on lipgloss sebum, scab-sequinned
Slide slowly out of his reach
To meet a flock of winged sanitary equipment
Shipped in especially
From the real world.
          There seems little else to say:
I can't hear him any more
This room is getting thicker
My stilettos are stuck to this melting pedestal
My lipstick has evaporated into stray kisses;
Morning has broken,

Fallen from the pedestal like a broken mirror
His voice cracks down the middle
And tomorrow night
The bad luck will be on me.

EIGHT HUNDRED YEARS DEEP

Edward Wilson (8)

Kevin Lennon (16)

Nightimage

I

There, as sparingly as possible,
Stood the past. As always,

There was no light to catch
The spade as it sank

Like a ship never built
Into the crusty soil and

Split the root that had
Lived seconds ago. He

Remembered daytime as he
Pulled back the spade.

He remembered the surplus
Of yesteryear or (the more

He thought about it)
Yesterday. He ploughed the

Field that night; he felt
He'd ploughed the world.

II

The child's eye lit the
Breakfast table. Inside,

(Far away) the son dug
Up the past. And perhaps,

The second before the root
Snapped, he believed in

The after-life or at least
The pre-life. Then the

Child blinked and he
Resumed digging.

III

Aeolus knew time. Between the iron
World of earth and the palaeolithic monument
Of ocean. Watching the relic of

Brightness reflect through water,
The Sisyphean talk of pessimism
Again finding itself in awe of

The cliff. He knew time.

His spade sank, his eyes old now;
Tired. He watched each fossil he
Dug up return to powder and hooves.

He thought of Phlebas, considered drowning
In the snow of his field;
He considered tasting black soil.

Considered breaking through.
Then the child blinked,
and he resumed digging.

Elizabeth Holden (10)

Guy Fawkes

Aching and cramped,
desperate and fearful,
curled in the stench of the Little Ease room.
Shackled by heavy chains,
bruised and stiff,
cold and hungry.

A rusty key turns in the lock,
rough hands drag him to the torture chamber.
He sees the rack, tries to resist, can't.

Manacles cut his wrists and ankles,
screams slice the dank air.
Saliva trickles from his bloodied mouth.

Bones wrenched from their sockets,
Information wrenched from his lips.

Charlotte Robinson (7)

*Church

I plod in, the door creaks behind me.
I stare at the organ buttons,
I see pipes that walk up, up, up,
Down, down, down.
I stare at the pulpit
It has a mat patterned, with a book on top.
An archway, carved into the stone, a rope plaited near
  by.
At each end a spear stands up straight.
Steps lead up.
I look down and I see the ground.
When you talk it echoes.
When you walk it sounds like a drip drip dripping tap.

Brian Adams (15)

Sam Robson (11)

Remembering Christie

Overgrown with brambles and nettles and filled with rusty corrugated iron, the house still stands at the end of Arran Quay.

This is the house where my great-grandfather was born.

South along the coast covered in ivy and moss the grey and glum structure of Tyrone House towers above the trees and thatched cottages.

Looking towards Tyrone House I remember the spring when I was 12 years old.

My mum and dad and I came over from London to see my great-granddaddy. It had been a cold winter and he had a chest infection or something like that.

He lived in the little cottage at the end of the road with his daughter, my great-aunt Gertie, who had never married. Once she had a short affair with a local fisherman who had moved away to Dublin.

We used to go up there once or twice a year.

My great-granddaddy and I had so much fun. He was a tall broad healthy old man with a weathered clean-shaven face. He had a full crop of white hair and black eyebrows. His eyes were almost black in a friendly way. His name was Christie and he had a great sense of humour.

He told me stories about local history and legends like the long black hand, a goblin that haunted a nearby churchyard. I especially enjoyed the Fion Macomhail stories.

My great-granddaddy and I used to go fishing at Tyrone House. In the 1920s when my great-granddaddy was 12 years old it was burnt out by the local people, when they heard rumours that Black and Tans were going to use it.

It stood as a blackened shell. It was a great place to play.

My great-grandfather and I went fishing on Tyrone Quay. We always took Tricks, his little fox terrier. Tricks used to roll around in the soft bouncy grass trying to catch flies, while my gramps and I sat on the rocky ledge of the quay eating sandwiches and drinking lemonade and Guinness. Granddad liked a spot of porter.

It was a nice friendly quay; the rocks were covered in gold and green lichens which felt like tortoise skin. When the tide came in the water would cover the grass and pink seathrift. Granddad and I never caught anything so instead we would pick mussels, oysters, winkles and whelks, and sometimes seaweed.

When we arrived that spring the house seemed quieter. Tricks was miserable, my aunt was miserable, my gran was miserable, my mum was making a fuss. Something was not right. I was allowed to go and see my great-grandpa who was tucked in his bed. It made me cry just thinking about his sad, pale lonely face. When I talked to him he just groaned and stared at me, as if to say:

"Please leave, son. I don't want you to see me like this."

I understood so I went back downstairs and listened to Galway Bay FM. I sat there thinking and crying about him. My grandma came downstairs and suggested I go for a walk with Tricks. So I did. I decided to go to Tyrone Quay. It was strange going without my granddad.

When I got there it was high tide, Grandpa's favourite time; he would say, "The higher the tide, the bigger the catch." This was a load of Lathabradgies anyway.

I was skimming stones when I noticed a young lad about the same age as me stumbling along the rocky shore carrying a bucket. I'd never met him before but he looked familiar. He waved at me so I waved back. As he walked he picked things up and put them in the bucket. He was wearing a flat cap, shirt and waistcoat and trousers. I thought he was dressed strangely. As he came up to me I said hello and asked him where he lived. "Along by Arron Quay," he said.

I thought he must mean one of the houses further inland from my granddad's. Tricks, who normally distrusted strangers, seemed excited to see the boy and kept on jumping up and wagging his tail.

The boy pointed up at Tyrone House which was silhouhetted against the pink and blue sky.

"Did you hear about the Black and Tans coming?" he said.

"Well yes," I laughed. "But that was a long time ago; my granddad told me about it."

The boy sat down on the rocks next to me and began skimming stones. In his bucket he had mussels, winkles and a bit of dulse. We talked about the fish and the house and that this was his favourite place.

It was getting dark so I decided to go home. I bid my new friend farewell. He insisted I take the bucket of shellfish.

As I was leaving I asked him his name. "Christie," he shouted as he waved goodbye.

When I got home my mum was waiting at the door; she was in tears. She hugged me and whispered in my ear, "Your great-grandpappy died a few hours ago, son."

Now I'm grown up and have my own son. I take him fishing at Tyrone Quay and remember Christie.

Paniz Shahkarami (13)

*The Hour of Execution

In the door-lock, a key turned.

A smile slithered onto his lips,
Like the dance of the water on the ceiling
From the light of the sun.

In the door-lock, a key turned.

Outside,
The pleasant colour of moist dawn,
As a lost note,
Looking, roaming
over the holes of the bamboo instrument
In search of its home . . .

In the door-lock, a key turned.
A smile danced onto his lips,
Like the water onto the ceiling
When the sun shines on it.

In the door-lock,
A key turned.

Jessica Goodacre (10)

The Hedaby Man

Couched in peat,
Preserved, the body lies
As though asleep,

Fingers clenched in pain
Like old birds' claws,

Skull cracked
Like a chipped cup,

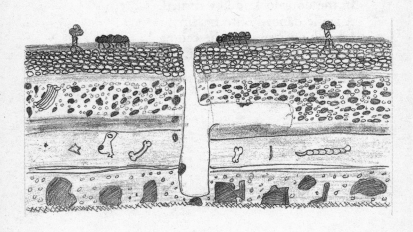

Kelly Garrison (12)

The stomach shrunken
To a purse of seeds,

Spine twisted
Into a hank of rope,

Wrist like a
Frail glass stalk,

Mouth lipped
As brittle bark,

Couched in peat,
Preserved, the body lies
As though asleep.

Peter Mitchell (13)

*Clearance

You will not find the village
If you look for years.
It is marked on no map;

But I found it
Walking among dead rocks
That I suddenly realised
Sprouted in patterns

It must have had a name.
Sprouting from the heather
Near the lichened sea-rocks
The blackhouses rested
Accumulating nettles
The rich lazybeds now gone

Here was a door,
Here was the turf wall
Here the rounded end.
Here where the animals sheltered
Here perhaps a box-bed
        Where generations loved, were born, died.

Here the blackened hearth stone,
The centre of the house
(It was lit the day the house
Was built, quenched when it fell)
They sat in a circle
Around it:
Watching the clammy peat smoulder rust
Their faces lit with the glow;
Speech moving back and forth

Ever across this fire
This blackened, weathered slab, now dead.

Perhaps she is still there
On nights when you could be tricked
Into believing that nothing ever
Happened here and innocence reigned . . .
The dark-haired woman of the house
Smooring, raking the embers,
Levelling them with her fingers
Intoning the smooring prayer
With loving care

Over this lifeless, faded
Stone.

Nisha Doshi (9)

*Eight Hundred Years Deep

Eight hundred years deep
Sleep the fragile fragments of the forgotten past;
And so, piercing and probing
The reluctant land,
The spades and shovels dig
And the buckets fill,
To be emptied of the centuries
Until, we reach the age of Medieval monks.
Then, heaving and hauling,
The unearthed years are carried away;
And we begin to gently
Sift and sieve the soil,
With our bare hands,
Revealing
Pieces of pot and shards of clay,
Which discarded, timeworn and torn,
Were the rubbish of some earlier day.
Then, tingling with triumph,
We brush the remaining crumbs of time away
And tenderly hold our treasured finds,
Which had lain hidden and asleep,
Eight hundred years deep.

Nisha Doshi (9)

Andrew Sayer (15)

MATCH OF THE DAY

Leon Gleadall

Michelle Long (16)

*Match of the Day

What a match this should be.
The final of the matrimonial cup.
The atmosphere here can only be classed as one of ter
as the players enter the stadium.

The whistle is blown
and the battle begins.

Doubt kicks off with a long pass to Suspicion.
Trust tries to take possession but
                    Suspicion gets through and chips it to
Lies
    who's looking for
                        Deceit . . . he's found him.
Deceit makes a break for goal and Veracity is nowhere
    to be seen.
And this is an excellent piece of football from Deceit.
Reconciliation's getting ready in goal . . . Deceit
    shoots . . . Oh my goodness it's come off the crossbar
        and is cleared away by Respect.
And now there's some superb passing going on between
    Faithfulness and
Loyalty in midfield
        but here comes Denial with a reckless tackle on
    Trust.
The whistle has gone and this surely must be a booking
    for Denial . . .
Yes – Compromise is calling him over.
Denial is pleading his innocence but there's a card coming
    out . . .
It's yellow!
Denial with his third yellow card of the season,
And a free kick has been given.
Love, the captain, is to take it.
Play resumes but the ball is intercepted by Lust who
    passes to Infidelity.
Now, this could be dangerous if he can get past
    Conscience . . .
                    who sends the ball out of play.

It's Jealousy to take the throw in
                            and it's taken up by Pride,
            who makes a
break down the right wing, but is brought down by
    Humility.
Pride stays down . . . and . . . I think . . .
                            yes, there's an injury here.
Pride is injured
            and is helped off the field.
A substitution will have to be made . . .
Self-esteem has been brought on.
Now Deceit comes into the picture,
                            this time aided by Lies,
                            who makes a
superb cross to Infidelity . . . he shoots . . . he scores . . .
No, wait . . . one of the Children has raised the offside
    flag . . .
the goal is disallowed.

And we're into stoppage time . . .
Compromise checks his watch . . .
The final whistle blows
            and at full time neither team has managed to
                score . . .

There will have to be a re-match . . .

Matthew Barnard (12)

Lucinda Morris (7)

*Persuading my Mother

I've tried to persuade my mother
Loads AND loads of times
To let me have a guinea pig
But she just says NO!
I WANT! I WANT A GUINEA PIG!
I would shout.
Once my friend Charlotte
Did a play for her,
And can you guess what it was about?
A poor little guinea pig without a home.
But it did not work.
Next we tried a treasure hunt
The treasure was lots and lots of notes
Which said, please please CAN I
Have a guinea pig?
But it did not work either.
So that was the end of that.
I could try writing a poem about it,
Then maybe she'd say yes.

Nisha Doshi (9)

*A Mouthful of Manhattan

Tantalising smells, spicy and strong,
Wrap themselves around us
And reel us in,
Like fish on an aromatic line,
Towards the kerbside kitchens
Of the street vendors' stands.
Queues of crisp, dark-suited men,
Fresh from air-conditioned offices,
Mingle with the garish shorts and shirts
Of the sweaty, suntanned tourists.
All eyes are focused on the feast
Being cooked in the humid New York heat.
Sausages, the size of cucumbers,
Sizzle inside their skins;
Pretzels, the size of dinner plates,
Plaited in salty rings;
Burgers in seeded buns,
Dripping with fried onions.

Nisha Doshi (9)

While the sun squints,
Sending shafts of red-hot spears
Between the stiff, skyscraper silhouettes,
Trucks and taxis and limousines
Tear past, oblivious
To the mouthwatering mountains
Of charcoaled chicken,
Roasted nuts
And sugared doughnuts;
Oblivious, to the star
Of the Manhattan street vendors:
Omar,
"The falafel man".

With a flourish,
He ladles streams of eggplant sauce
Over fistfuls of salad
And flattened fried falafel,
Stuffed into huge pitta bread pouches,
Which never seem to get smaller,
No matter how much you chew!
Drooling, we attach ourselves
To the end of his queue,
Hypnotised by the tantalising smells,
Spicy and strong,
Which wrapped themselves around us
And drew us along,
To lunch at Omar's,
For a mouthful of Manhattan.

Geraint Jenkins (9)

Mahlete-Tsigé Getachew (16)

*Fish in the Sea

Plastic, Amber discovered, could smirk. The phone was definitely looking at her sidelong. She reached for the remote control and grimly flicked over.

I can conquer this, she told herself. I can. I don't need Greg. I don't need Molly to tell me I don't need Greg. What I really want to do right now more than anything else is watch this brilliant programme about . . . about the mating habits of grebes.

The phone preened nonchalantly. She half expected it to start whistling.

"Just because it's Saturday and I always phone Molly at this time, it doesn't mean that I'm going to phone her this week," she informed the phone.

Her voice plummeted into the silence and lay dying at the foot of the Cliffs of Insanity.

The phone smugly picked its teeth. She glared at it. However, it is easier to outstare a baby than it is to out-stare a plastic telephone. Particularly one that knows it's going to win.

The phone was definitely going to win. It was, after all, Saturday and ever since Greg, Amber found that the days tended to run into each other, a long grey blur stretching dismally on. It was also true that Amber phoned Molly at this time every Saturday. Molly was the only one of her *friends* Amber still spoke to after What Happened With Greg. Away with ambiguity; Molly was the only *friend* who let Amber speak to her.

"I'll spare her this week," Amber announced. "Our con-versations are getting to be fairly predictable." The phone raised an infinitely superior eyebrow. "But I expect you know that."

I can't help eavesdropping, the phone whined. *What else am I supposed to do – malfunction? Then you wouldn't be able to reach even Molly.*

"True," Amber conceded, "but you could have the decency not to laugh at our conversations."

"Conversations"? The phone sniggered. *Try "mono-logues".*

Again, the phone had a point. Amber would talk and Molly would coo, then Molly would faithfully dart in to reassure Amber that there were plenty more fish in the sea and Amber would dourly agree – adding that they were all piranhas or they all slipped through the net.

More recently, with the advent of Terry in Molly's life, Amber found that Molly had less time for her. She would

127

barely conceal her boredom, cutting the familiar dialogue indecently short and snapping at Amber impatiently like an aggravated terrier. Amber could feel Molly slipping away from her and this just made her loneliness more asphyxiatingly absolute.

I'm not speaking to my telephone, I'm concentrating on grebes, Amber thought firmly. Grebes are of foremost importance at this particular moment in my life. It is imperative that I saturate myself with knowledge of their mating habits. She held down the volume button on the remote control. The sound increased exponentially.

"Grebes are one of the few animals," the presenter boomed through the cheated winds, "that, human-like, have one lifelong partner."

Lifelong partner. Greg. How could he?

There is only so much torment a person can take. Amber snatched up the telephone and began to dial furiously, grief exploding in her throat. In a strange detached way, she heard herself whimpering.

"Molly, I can't take it any more – Molly, I've got to do something – Molly, please come over, I'm so *lonely* . . ."

"Hello?"

It was a male voice, impossibly smooth and lighter than air. He must be Terry, Amber thought distractedly. Molly spoke about him often. Too often.

"Hi, this is Amber. May I speak to Molly?"

"Sorry, no Molly here." Butterflies wove patterns between his words.

"Wrong number, then." Her own voice sounded thin and strained in her ears. She cleared her throat and tried again. "Sorry."

"No problem. Bye."

Amber hung up slowly, marvelling at the incredible goldness of his voice. It was audible ice cream, nectar for the ears. If contentment were a song, his would be the tender baritone to sing it. If sculpture could speak, it would be the voice of Michelangelo's *David*.

Graceless Greg hadn't sounded like that.

She dialled Molly again, lingering over each number, savouring the memory of his voice and wondering what stray glance of capricious Lady Luck had permitted her – *her* – a whole instant of pleasant surprise. Of course, she thought bitterly, being Amber, I hung up. I taint everything I touch. I don't deserve to be happy.

Amber, *happy*?

She tried to muster a cynical laugh but her throat was too constricted.

Great, now I can't even be melodramatic.

"Hello?"

Suddenly, the voice wasn't a fantasy any more, it was there, in its full glory, seeping through the fibres, pouring through the receiver. Her bitterness melted away like snow in the summer, her head perked up like a flower brought into abundant sunlight.

"You're not Molly."

A delightfully rich chuckle. "It's Amber again, isn't it? Are you sure you dialled properly?"

"Oh yes – I dialled especially slowly and I know Molly's number off by heart, I took extra care not to—"

That slow, indulging laughter again. It rolled over her like the smell of spiced home-made bread. Flustered, Amber realised he was teasing her. "It must be crossed lines," she finished lamely.

"It must be," agreed Tones-Of-Ambrosia.

"I'll try her again. Bye."

She hung up quickly this time, not wanting to prolong the sweet sorrow of losing her beloved. She flicked distractedly from channel to channel, finally resettling on the grebe documentary. It was infinitely more bearable now that she was blissfully replaying the conversation.

He was young, she decided, not much older than her. His voice was mellifluous and mellow, mercurial and light. Too quick to be a philosopher, too slow to be a fool. He was a blade sharpened on gossamer silk but wise enough to know that he could harm, and he chose not to.

If he was a god, Amber dreamily concluded, he would be bronze Apollo of music and poetry, with godlight blazing from his body and sunlight pouring through his lips. He would say "Amber" and smile, then reach out his hand . . .

Amber's eyes snapped open.

He had said "Amber".

She closed her eyes and concentrated, replaying his words. "It's Amber again . . ."

He had paused on "Amber", letting the syllables drop off his tongue.

Amber turned the TV off and drummed her fingers against the sofa arm.

He had remembered her name.

He was young.

He was pleasant, amusing, relaxed, golden-voiced . . .

He was alone and at home on a Saturday night.

Amber's fingers crept towards the telephone. Molly had always said there were plenty more fish in the sea, that Greg wasn't the only man in the world.

She lunged for the phone before it could inch away any further and determinedly dialled Molly's number, praying with her whole being that the technicians hadn't corrected the fault.

First ring.

Amber crossed her fingers.

Second ring.

Amber watched the seconds tick past on her watch and felt her heart beating a counter-rhythm.

Third ring.

"Hello?"

Amber uncrossed her fingers.

"Three guesses."

Laughter. Almost – Amber thought swiftly – relieved laughter. As if he had been waiting for the phone to ring.

"Looks like you're not going to get through to Molly tonight."

"Looks like I'm not."

"You'll just have to make do with me."

"Possibly. You've got to impress me first."

More laughter, from both of them, then talk. They were hesitant at first, two anonymous voices relayed by pure glass fibres, but then something in the other's tone – a thread of sorrow, a muted note in the melody of their voice – prompted them to share a little, then a little more, then a lot.

They chatted loosely, exchanged light banter. They argued heatedly over the rights and wrongs of vegetarianism (she made a brief reference to inviting him to a vegetarian restaurant) and rambled through his work as a chemical researcher (he casually suggested she might want to look around his research labs one day). They touched lightly on past loves, and future hopes, each of them sensitive enough to realise that this was not the time to reopen closed wounds.

All good things come to an end, and as the church bells rang eleven, Amber stirred from her recumbent position. Unconsciously, she had curled up on the sofa like a cat, the telephone cradle lovingly nested on her shoulder. She smothered a yawn in the cushion and stretched her legs.

He cleared his throat.

"Listen, I—" they both began. They stopped and laughed. Again.

"You first."

"No, you."

"All right. It's been great talking to you, Amber."

"Likewise you. I don't believe we spoke for so long."

"It only felt like a minute . . ." His voice tailed wistfully off.

"I suppose I'd better go now."

He sighed. "I suppose."

"It was fun, though."

"Yes."

"Goodbye, then."

"Goodbye, Amber."

She waited for him to hang up, heard the tender *click* as the receiver was replaced. She sighed and cupped her face in her hands. Incongruously, Amber realised that she'd laughed more in that too brief conversation than she had in the whole of the week. She had found herself being inexorably drawn out like a golden wire, and she hadn't resisted.

It was almost as if her loneliness might end.

He had touched the core of her being as no other man had before. He had told her enough to let her know that he too shared her loneliness and yet together they had broken the barrier of pain. Surely he wouldn't mind if she rang him again? Yes, Amber decided, she would ring him tomorrow. They would talk some more. She would ring him tomorrow.

Suddenly, she was stricken with an urgency she could not comprehend. She had to ring him now. It was a powerful compulsion that would not be ignored. She could not pent up these alien feelings any longer. He had to know. She needed to hear his voice now, saying her name as he'd said it before.

Amber.

Hands shaking, she tried to dial the number. Twice she made a mistake and started again, cursing her folly. Still shaking, she rehearsed her lines: "What are you doing next

Saturday then?" "You never did tell me your name." "Do you believe in true love?" They were all incredibly inadequate but they would have to do. She fought to control her breathing as the phone rang.

The receiver was lifted. Amber plunged in before her courage failed her.

"Listen, there's something I meant to tell you—"

"Hi, Amber," said Molly. "Did you watch the film, then?"

David Pitts (12)

Absurd Words

Imagine a story where:
Similes are all different,
Personification is dead,
Interjections are sensible remarks,
And collective nouns have separated.

Imagine a story where:
Verbs have stopped doing things,
Adjectives are boring,
Adverbs are subtract-verbs,
And the alphabet is mbludje!

Imagine a story where:
Prepositions are lost,
Full stops are empty,
Sentences are paragraphs,
And paragraphs are sentences.

Imagine a story where:
Headlines are shy,
Pronouns forget people's names,
Conjunctions have become unstuck,
And speech marks have run out of things to say!

Lauren Coffey (13)

Ellen Coffey (8)

*Sledging

It's a slippery struggle to the top,
The soft snow all worn down
and smooth as glass.
Aching legs don't want to climb again,
Fingers, numbed by icy wind, won't grip the string,
My heart is drumming,
Breath smokes from my mouth,
And then I'm in my sledge, the way is clear,
I streak downhill so fast, too fast to scream,
The world's a blur, snow showers in my face,
Clinging on, I'm waiting for the crash
Which doesn't come,
I've landed safely and I know
That when I've caught my breath I'll climb again.

Henrietta Selman (13)

*Can't Walk, Can't Dance, Can't Run, Can't Play

"I am going to be late for Tara, I'm going to be late," was running a marathon around my head. I pulled my coat from the banister and shouted to my mother. I think she shouted "be careful". I say "I think" because I mostly remember being preoccupied with the fact I was supposed to be meeting my best friend, in the High Street in five minutes. I am usually very streetwise, and can often be found tugging one of my friends back if they try to cross on a red man and scowl at those who cross the road without looking. So why did I run into the middle of the road? Why is life full of dramatic irony? And why did a car have to run me over? I can remember thinking, "Tara's going to kill me." Little did I know that a car was almost about to do the same. I could hear hooting and I saw the great metal object come looming towards me. I can remember seeing the driver's look of horror on his face and I remember feeling mine. I couldn't move. My body was screaming "Come on, get out of the way." But my legs wouldn't work. I heard screeching brakes, a horrible noise like a nail down a blackboard. I screamed. I fell. My head hurt. I felt tired. I shut my eyes. I could hear a commotion, people shouting. Someone crying. I felt as if I was spinning. You're going to die now, Heni, I thought. You're going to die. Sirens. Maybe. I don't know. I was so tired. I wanted to be sick. Mummy. I wanted my mummy. "I am going to be late for Tara." Black.

I did not wake up like you do in the morning. One minute you are asleep and the next you are awake. I must have been conscious for about five minutes without being aware

I was. I remember the air was fresh and cool. It was my oxygen mask. My head hurt. I felt wet. I ached. Lights were shone in my eye. My name was repeated. I could not talk. I thought someone had grabbed my throat, but I was wrong. A female was talking about lifting me up. I felt people's fingers slide around my body. They hurt me. I cried. I was lifted up and placed on an uncomfortable bed. They were telling me about painkillers and I felt a sting in my hand. I went to sleep.

When I woke up, this time it was like waking up in the morning but for some reason I did not feel fresh and rested. I felt groggy and I hurt so much. I heard beeping. Machines. I heard my parents trying to converse with me, trying to get a reaction.

The next few days lay about in an oblivion. I didn't know who or where I was. When I was moved away from the Intensive Care and into the ward I felt a lot better. I was learning to cope with the pain. After all, the morphine injections were not that far apart. I felt numb. In my legs. Where were they?

That was about the time I told my mother. At first I wished I hadn't. She told a nurse and I had lots of painful tests. During the weeks I had begun to feel better. My friends and teachers had come to see me. I was worried that Tara would be angry for me standing her up that day but suprisingly she wasn't! I know that seems strange now but then I used to worry about the smallest things. My friends never gave up on me. They used to come regularly. I discovered that I preferred shots of gossip instead of morphine; it kept me in touch with things outside a hospital. I am not easily shocked and can quite easily prepare myself for all kinds of things, like when I found out that my dog had to be put down. To be fair there was and still is nothing that could ever prepare me for my life-changing news.

"You are never going to walk again, Henrietta." That was it. Those words seem to signal to me the end of my life. Although that is not true in the chronological order, for the first feeling was that of incredulity. I didn't believe them. They were lying. A cruel joke for all the bad things I had done in my life. I tried to kick, wave my arms and scream. An immense anger welled up inside me like a tear in its tear duct. I could not speak. What had I done? "It was my fault. No, my mother's. If I had never told her that I could never feel my legs, then she would never have gone and told the nurse, I would not have had to have the tests which found out that I could not walk and then I would never be in the situation that I was. I could just have pretended that I could walk." Of course that was impossible but I did not care. I needed someone to blame.

I look back on the feelings I had then by reading my diary. I find it hard to believe that I ever thought that, but when I think about it again I can see that to me then it did make sense. Over the weeks that followed I shall never forget the pain from the frustration that seemed to overtake my mind and soul. How I refused to see my friends. How I treated my parents. How many tears I used to cry. How long I used to lie awake each night. At first I cheated myself. I told myself that it was a process called self-denial. How, the longer that I did not walk, the easier it would become when I finally tried. Of course there was no day that I would ever just get up and walk. It was just my imagination. The day I finally accepted it was after a few weeks of torture, which I used to do to myself. I would spend several hours at a time watching the sports channel. Watching how they could run and play and walk and dance. Dance was the worst thing because there is something I never mentioned. I was Grade 4 ballet, with "potential". It was something I had done since I was three and something I loved. It was a time where I forgot about everything and the way I danced was about the inner me. Over the months of the accident I had forgotten about dance until I saw it one day on television and the anger and the incomprehensibility of the whole situation made me cry and do something very stupid. I tried to get up. As I pushed my arms against the machine I hated so much, my wheelchair, I felt a great sense of pride, but that was soon diminished as I landed on the floor. I stayed there for some time. Thinking. Wondering. Then I called for Mum.

My doctor and physiotherapist came round that afternoon. They told me about all these clubs I could join which since then I have done. I am now in the Under 15s basketball team which plays against other wheelchair teams. I have learnt that being in a wheelchair is not the end of the world as it seems at first, and to remember that there is someone always worse off than you and perhaps you should think about them and to remember that once all those stormy clouds have been blown away there will be sunshine and a beautiful, warm, clear day.

GAZELLE, GALAGO, GANDER
AND GIBBON

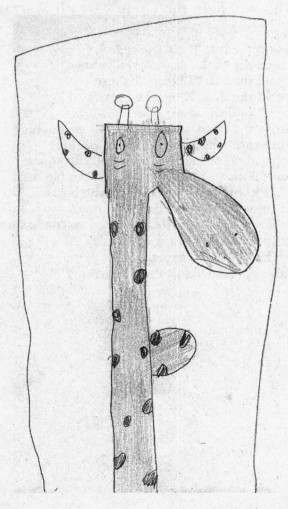

Dominic Clerici (7)

Rosie Gamble (11)

*Who will Sign the Dodo's Death Warrant?

"I," said the rat. "I ate the eggs."
"I," said the eagle. "I took the young."
"I," said the cat. "I killed the birds."
"I," said the dog. "I ate the birds."
"No, I," said the man.
"I drove the ships with the rats all on board,
I didn't care when they all went ashore.
I didn't mind when the eagle took the young.
I didn't notice when my cat killed the birds.
I didn't know when my dog ate the birds.
I felt proud when I shot the last one.
I felt good when I stuffed it full of cotton wool.
I felt great when I put it on display.
Now, hand me the paper.
I shall sign the Dodo's death warrant!"

Sasha Penney (11)

Ashley Dietrich (6)

Sam Keeble (5)

*Sometimes I Scare my Mummy

Sometimes I scare my mummy
when I turn into a spider.
She runs away.
Daddy tries to put me down
the toilet. I shout,
"Dad, don't!"

Sarah Lea (11)

*Hot Pig

A stream of crystal bliss
Cascades from a rusty bucket.
A film of precious glass
Glides effortlessly over raw sandpaper skin.
Cold tears of luxury
Are balm to a blistering back.
Sparkling towers of spray
Rebound off his body,
His sweltering snout soothed,
As well-worn trotters
Sumptuously sink into aqueous mud.
Beneath the heavenly splash,
A glorious grunt of gratitude
And a twitch of a twisted tail
Accompany a huge smile of great relief.

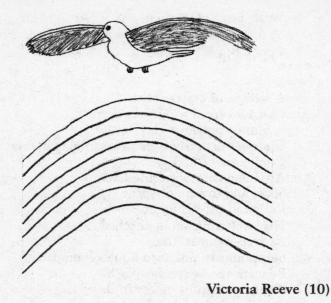

Victoria Reeve (10)

Jonathan Cartwright (9)

*The Christmas Dove

Some people invite aunts and uncles for Christmas; we invited a dove. We found him frozen, half dead on the bird table in a terrible blizzard.

Papa picked him up and brought him inside. He placed the dove in the cat basket (the sort of basket used to carry a cat to the vet), then he put the basket near the fire. After several hours the dove responded to the warmth and ate the food we gave him.

The next day Nana carried him up to the top bedroom in the basket, where he could look through the window

146

at the other birds outside in the snow. When fresh food was put in the basket the dove escaped onto the desk. He was returned to the basket. Nana decided it was time for him to be taken outside and released. The basket door was opened but the dove would not go. It was freezing cold; he huddled in the back of the basket. Back up to the bedroom he went.

Nothing happened on the third day except the dove upset his food and paddled in his drinking water. He seemed happy.

On the fourth day of the dove's visit the weather was milder. We went shopping and hoped Sylvester, our 18-year-old cat, would not discover the dove. We got back to find Sylvester asleep as usual. The dove had upset his drinking water and overturned his food container. He was standing on his food dish to have a better view outside.

After lunch we took the basket in the garden and opened the basket door. We waited. "Come on Dilly," I whispered. "You can do it." The dove flew into the air, he landed on a pole, preening his feathers for one whole hour. From the window I watched and waited; the Christmas dove soared over the roof tops to the trees far beyond.

Alexandra Baylor (6)

In the Whale's Tummy

I can hear his heart beating,
the water spurting out of his hole.
I can hear gobbled fish.
I feel scales.
I see puddles.
I see his bones.
I put my hand on his heart.
It is red.
It goes goggle, goggle, goggle.
I want Mummy to turn the light on.

Nicola Talbuys (14)

Cherdana Saggers (6)

Bobby Bristow (6)

Bedtime

Sometimes, when I don't
want to go to sleep
I turn into an elephant.
I squirt water with my trunk.
I stamp on my bed.
Mummy says, "What's this elephant doing here?"
I say, "It's not an elephant. It's me."
"Well get into bed then!" she says.

149

Susanna Garwood (8)

*Paint-Pot Parrot

Somewhere high above the clouds, where the sun is always shining, is God's workshop. This is where God made light, sky, land, sea, every kind of plant, sun, moon, stars and finally all the animals.

Now, the animals were very different then because they were all beige and not a bit exciting to look at. What's more, God hadn't decided what colours they were going to be, or even what they were going to be called. God was sitting hunched up over His workbench very tired, trying to decide what to call the animals, and what colour they were going to be. At last He thought:

"I will give each animal a name and colour in alphabetical order!"

So He started, with aardvark, then adder, then alligator, then anchovy, then ant, then anteater, then ape and armadillo.

Meanwhile, at the door of God's workshop, there stood a large nosy bird who was always being cheeky and poking his beak into where it wasn't wanted. All the time that God was painting and naming, this rude bird was pushing the other birds and animals and shouting at the top of his harsh voice.

"I don't like the colour He's painted you! What a silly name! Aardvark! Nobody will *ever* be able to spell that!"

Later God was painting budgie while the baboon watched.

"He should be purple!" screeched the bird. "Do him purple, go on, do him purple!"

"Will you be quiet, you interfering bird!" yelled God in a booming voice.

150

As He turned to speak to the bird, He accidentally brushed the baboon's newly painted pink bottom with the blue brush that He had been painting the budgie with!

"Now look what I've done," said God, throwing the blue paint pot at the bird.

"Sorry, sorry," sniggered the bird, getting splashed with blue paint down his chest!

"Go away, bird," said God crossly. "When I need your advice I'll ask for it."

The bird sat quietly in the shadows for a while, all the time muttering to himself and making comments under his breath.

"It should be orange," or shouting, "EARWIG! EARWIG! Who wants to be called earwig, I ask you?!"

At last, by the time God came to the "F"s, the bird just couldn't help it any more.

"Hey!" he yelled, as God was doing the flamingo's feathers. "That bird's beak should be blue – it's obvious!"

"How many times do I have to tell you, bird," said God in His biggest voice. "Don't distract me!"

(In fact He was so distracted He had accidentally put the flamingo's body back on his legs the wrong way round.)

"Sorry, mate," said the bird, laughing up his wing at the flamingo walking off with his knees bending backwards.

"Rude bird," yelled God, hurling the red paint pot at the bird who flew off, getting the paint on his wings and head.

The bird hid up a tree as God continued with the "F"s.

"Now," said God to a little hoppy creature. "You shall be known as 'FROG' and you shall be green. Sit still for goodness sake, can't you!"

Up in the tree the bird laughed himself off the branch and fell into the green paint.

"You again," thundered God. "Clear off until I call you!" He moved on to the "G"s, grumbling as he worked through gazelle, galago, gander and gibbon to the giraffe.

"Blooming bird," He muttered. "This is difficult work, and needs concentration."

He thought hard for a minute. "You, giraffe, shall be yellow with a brown mane and tail, I think. Doesn't that sound nice?"

"Sounds absolutely horrible to me," said a cheeky voice from behind Him. "Anyone can see that he should be green like the trees. His neck is far too long as well. He looks a right banana, and will look more of one if he is painted yellow!"

God was *so* cross He threw the yellow paint at the bird and upset the *brown* paint all over the poor giraffe, who was spotty for ever afterwards because he was too scared to go back to be re-painted.

"This is *too* much," roared God. "Go away, bird, this is your last warning. Don't you dare come back until *I* call you!"

This time the bird decided he had better keep out of God's way until He had calmed down. He didn't want to be unmade!

He sat sulking in the bushes as God carried on working His way through the alphabet and gradually getting His temper back.

"Oh dear," said God to Himself as He painted the hedgehog. "You're a bit prickly. Maybe I could have made you a *bit* better. Hmm," He commented as He finished the jackal. "Maybe you're a bit beastly. You're a bit hairy," said God as He named the llama. "Monkey, your arms do seem to be a bit long."

God thought about all these things as He went on working and at last He called out:

"Come on, you." He turned and looked at the paint-splashed bird who sat on His hand.

"Well I don't need to paint you at all," He said thoughtfully. "Maybe I didn't get every animal *quite* right, but at least the world will be an exciting place to live in when I've finished. You will be called parrot and if you ask *me*, it's a jolly good thing you're so many bright colours. We will all be able to see you coming before you stick your beak into our business."

The parrot laughed his harsh laugh.

"I'm the most lovely bird in the forest," he called as he flew off. "Designed my *own* plumage, I did!"

Can *you* think of a more nosy bird than the parrot??

RIBBONS OF MOSS-GREEN

Jason Wright (12)

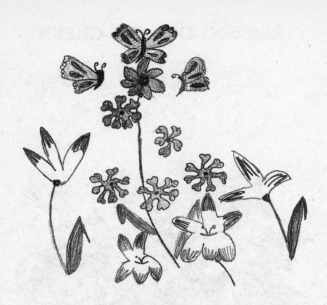

Gemma Holden (12)

Daisy Corbett (6)

*Painted Petals

Toblerone-shaped yellow seeds
curved round a glow worm of lime.
Butterfly wings spread
from pink to red
like watercolours running
into space.

Strawberry and raspberry star shapes
cling to custard
and peach petals.

Branches lead
from a mustard sun.

Overlapping leaves protect
the forest flowers.

Clear crinkled skin
like seaweed veins
sliding to the centre
of the painted path,
shading the blooms.

Octopus's tentacles
bend upwards.
Hairs like fine dust
flow along the stalk.

Spindly dry roots
push through delicate winding roads.

Red and gold,
cold Indian pot,
hard against my warm hands.

The scent reaches up to Heaven,
reminds me of Spring.

Primula thinks it's Queen.

Ellen Coffey (8)

*Dunwich

The heather was a purple quilt
Making a bed for the setting sun,
We took our picnic and watched Shakespeare on the
    Heath,
Till it became quite dark, mysterious and cold,
Another world for night-time animals.

It is evening now,
The sky has pinkened and turned black,
We breathe sea air, escape the city's fumes,
My daughter skips ahead, I stroll behind,
The years have passed, but this feels just the same,
The heather scratches our legs,
As, in darkness, we walk to the car.

Victoria Levell (11)

Rainbow Rainbow

The rainbow was first made
when God bought Jesus
some felt-tip pens and
he scribbled across the sky.

It is like a bridge
spanning cloud to cloud,
only appearing after the rain.

A rainbow is a gate to heaven.
You pass through this world
to get there.

The rainbow is God's mouth,
but you only see it
when he's standing on his head.
He doesn't do this often
but when he does, he's happy.

Maybe it's a bridge
from our world to another.

It is Jesus's slide
which he only gets out to play on
after the rains have been.

It is Mary's hair ribbons
floating in the sky.

Tina Earl (10)

Emily McIntosh (9)

*Midas

Midas is walking,
He sees:

A child skipping
And shouting papa.

Roses, cherry framed
Growing up a wall.

A river's ripples
Circling in the shadows.

Holly leaves,
sharpened horns,
Berries flushed.

The oak tree
Waving its branches in the wind.

Then, the Golden Touch:

The child, mouth wide open
No sound coming out.

The roses hardening
As their scent disappears.

The river rock solid,
Ripples like glass circles.

The holly brittle
Like a star point.

The oak tree
Set like cement
On the forest floor.

Daisy Corbett (6)

*Agglestone Rock, Studland Bay

Shades of luminous green.
Chalk white like snow melting.
Long thin grass shoots from the boiling stone.
Dark pink heather in a circle of tiny houses.
Cold cave where the wind rushes outwards.
Flat slippery rocks.
I can see gorse through my empty window.
Burnt cracks scraped into orange steps.
Names everywhere telling you who you are.
Patterns smooth into shadowy lines.
I quietly creep into the dark shady tunnel.
Cobwebs trap ghost holes.
I stare at the face of a bat watching me.
Purple slits crunch into stone.
I find the blue smooth sheet of ocean.
I burst out of the hot desert.
A family of crickets in the tall ferns.
Prickles point at the side of a slim track.
I slide through a passageway of undergrowth.
I turn round.
The Mushroom bending over.
The witch's rock
is there for ever.

Harriet Earis (15)

Jugs on a Welsh Dresser

A coloured crockery of wind catches
At the crooked edges of hawthorn hooks.
The glaze of clouds pours towards the dull hills
As the gusts churn the downpour,
Whisking the light drops to skim the edges of moorland.
Brimming bogs creep into sphagnum.

The inglenook cramps comfortably
As the smell of slate darkens on the room.
The settling flames gleam in the daylight dreams of
    shadows,
Rounding like cream porcelain proudly prized.
Fired logs sear the shadows
As handles of flames lick in milk-white dazzles of curves,
Caught in their gilded inlay.
In sharp, collected array, the drizzle jostles softly.

The patterned pottery of rain patters on the recessed
    window,
Shattering to splattering water.
Soaked ewes baa towards a loneliness of late lambs
Whilst the sky's ewer empties,
Washing the winded distance of foam stream.
Full-fed, it torrents pitchers of peaty waterfalls,
Pitching down to a far-off sea.

Emily Ward (17)

Outside the shrouded barns, the paleness of late
  tormentil
Weaves faded floral rims to the arching turf.
Colours of saturated harebells huddle round the bases of
  slopes
Whilst the ribbons of moss-green are traced
About the spilling apex of hillside.
Still just etched with a following line of silver, trickling.

Inside the farmhouse the low dresser wrestles with its
  jugs.
Just a merging ancestry of china,
Blandly watching the seconds drip.

Hannah Shroot (7)

Winter Witch

I freeze the ponds from water to ice
I make the rain fall from the sky
My breath smells like salty sea
I am the winter witch.
My anger makes the thunder roar
I play dominoes with icicles
I knock them down one by one
I am the winter witch!

Rachel Jamieson (6)

Alice McCabe (11)

Thistles

A crown of spikes,
A royal blossom of purple,
A barbed-wired stalk,
A farmer's plague,
A flower from hell,
A cousin of the nettle,
Yet with seeds like down from the hen,
A series of hot hedgehogs,
An eternal warrior with daggers of pride,
A warhorse's haughty plume.
They grow old like men becoming bald.
A spiteful fiend.
Never dying,
Never ending.
The thistle.

MRS HEAVENS HAS CURLY HAIR

Natalie Burns-Spence (14)

Angharad Guy (5)

*My New Miss

She sings songs
on a Saturday morning.
Mrs Heavens went to France
on a very early day.
Mrs Heavens has curly hair
and my new miss has
very, very, very straight hair.

My miss reads stories very good,
and she writes pictures on the wall,
and she rubs them all out on the window.
She does it all on a Saturday day.

She drives a car
and it's very, very oily,
and she puts oil in it,
and she oils the car and the tyres
so it goes fast.

Poppy Corbett (9)

Dad's Ties

Dad's got a tie for every occasion.
It's easy spotting him in a crowd.

Catherine wheel snowflake,
jean blue,
liberty touch,
jagged flowers
on a bright background.
At a hot Summer Fete,
Dad's under a tree
by the swings in Oakridge –
he'll use it as a fan
to cool down.

Mum says,
"Stroud's florist
should wear it
underneath his canvas."

Dad's got a tie for every occasion.
It's easy spotting him in a crowd.

Spotted
with Dalmatian dogs,
sat on checked rugs
or asleep in peace.
Dad's off
to The Dog Rescue centre –
he'll use it as a lead
for a speedy greyhound.

Mum says,
"Crufts' best of breed judge
should wear it."

Dad's got a tie for every occasion.
Its easy spotting him in a crowd.

Metallic blue,
slim tie.
Glistening glitter,
tinsel strips
catch the eye,
snatch the light.
Dad's dancing
on the disco day.
Head turning,
arms stretching,
legs kicking,
knees knocking,
feet tapping.
Dad's keeping cool
with his luminous
blue sweatband.

Mum says,
"The famous River Dancer,
Michael Flatley,
should wear it."

Dad's got a tie for every occasion.
It's easy spotting him in a crowd.

Ink spots
spread on a circus tent,
a parade of perfect clowns.

Dad's having fun,
marching and mixing
with the carnival.
He's up high,
riding on the elephant's back,
swatting wasps.

Mum says,
"The carnival Boss
should flirt
with the classy tie."

We're at the zoo,
lions roar,
armadillos snore,
anteaters lick,
zebras kick,
snakes glide.
Dad's on the slide –
but where's his tie?

Dad hasn't got a tie for this occasion.
I wonder why – he's wearing a bow tie.

Dad's got a bow tie for every occasion.
It's easy spotting him in a crowd.

Nisha Doshi (9)

*Walter

A small, frail man shuffles along the path, his back bent in the pouring rain, as he drags a wheelchair ramp from the garage. The huge, solid, wooden frame of the ramp towers above him and, as he battles against the wind, it looks as if the ramp might topple on to him. I watch from the window, across the road, warm and dry; I feel helpless, useless. He looks so weary and depressed and is already wet, even though it's only a few metres from the garage to his back door; for him, those few metres must seem like miles.

Thankfully, he reaches the door, at last, and lets the ramp drop down. He steps back a little and stares at it, as if he hates it. Then his whole body seems to sigh with relief and he turns, stiffly, his shoulders hunched, his back still bent, and slowly trudges back to the garage. Perhaps he doesn't notice the rain, perhaps he's too weary to care. All his movements seem to be in slow motion and seem to echo the tiredness in his face.

Under the shelter of the garage door, he stops to light his pipe. The wind catches a puff of smoke and carries it away. Walter doesn't seem to mind; he looks thoughtful and sad, quite different from the friendly man, who often comes over for a chat with Mum and never seems to run out of conversation.

Since his wife, Nancy, became paralysed, after a stroke two years ago, Walter often looks anxious. The cheeks of his thin, pale face are pinched, making his chin look pointed and sharp. Small folds of skin hang from his neck, loose and floppy. Deep wrinkles ripple along his frowning forehead and branch into many fine lines, which spread out, then gather around each eye, like the rays of the sun in a young child's drawing. His dark-rimmed glasses are usually perched halfway down his nose and he has a habit of peering over the top of them, when he's talking.

A band of very short, straight, silver-grey hair circles his shiny, bald head; but it's often hidden by his favourite, brown tweed hat, which he wears almost every day of the year: hot or cold, wet or dry!

He's wearing it, today. But he looks fragile and lonely: a small, tired man smoking his pipe, standing under the garage door, in the pouring rain. He must be quite strong, otherwise he'd never be able to do all the things he does for Nancy. But, he looks so sad and weary, I think life must be very hard for Walter and elderly people like him.

Sally Hartfield (12)

*The Sprinter

The sprinter
Tense
      Nervously swaying on the block
The moment
          Has arrived
Andonetwothreehe's
            Away
Flying focused
          Straight
How does it feel to come second?
No longer

      The best.

Poppy Corbett (9)

175

Thomas Brooks (8)

My Friend Peter

My friend Peter likes football,
He's a Christian;
He's got two goldfish
And he's my best friend at school!

Freckle face,
His hair like half a chestnut,
Blonde brown,
He's from a family of seven;
He has a coat that was his big brother Daniel's –
It's quite old,
It looks baggy,
I think it looks nice and cosy!

Abigail Hayhoe (10)

His big brother Daniel's rabbit died
And they had a funeral for him.
If I had a rabbit
I'd like to be with him when he died.

Good at drawing
He's very positive about things;
When he wants to do something
He does it –
He gets straight into the action of it:
He says "Oh WOW!"
He's a comedian!

My friend Peter
Has a hand that is a strange shape.
He's got two fingers and a thumb on one side
And the other side's ordinary.
His best birthday present
Was when the doctor told him
He didn't need to have another operation for six months.

Joanne Miller (8)

A Little Girl . . .

A little girl is sitting alone in a room.
It is pouring with rain outside.

I drew a picture of my friend with my finger pen
Outside the window, silver worms
were coming down the glass.

David Newman (11)

*The Family Gathering?

It was a typical family gathering at the White House. Our White House that is not President Clinton's, although if you saw my mam flapping about cleaning things that we don't normally bother to clean, you'd probably think that even if it wasn't the President's house, he must have been invited. Everybody else seemed to be.

The main problem, you see, is that there's nothing "typical" or even nearly "normal" about our family. It's not like other people's. It's not like the ones you read about in books either, although sometimes you get something that sounds a bit like ours in one of the Sunday papers. Anyway, we know who we all are (sometimes), but it's a bit difficult explaining to other people.

You see there's me and Mam, Pete, Peter and Joe and that's when it gets a bit confusing. Pete's my "sort of" stepdad and "the beasts" are my "sort of" stepbrothers. Actually it's Mam who call them "the beasts", so I do. She calls us all it really when she means the kids but I don't think she really means to include me. I mean, how can she when I'm perfect? It first came to be a big problem when I had to draw a family tree and I thought and thought about that and eventually drew a monkey puzzle. As it turned out, they didn't mean a real tree anyway but how was I to know? Have you noticed how teachers don't always explain things properly, then they say you don't listen. That's always happening to me and I do listen. So anyway, there was that and the name problem. Mam and me have one surname and they have another. And it wouldn't be so bad if they weren't called Adams as a second name. It means that we get known as the Adams

Syreeta Stewart (16)

Family and even if there's only one "d" in our Adams it doesn't really help because when people say "the Adams Family" who can tell how many "d"s there are? In Adams you don't hear the double "d" anyway, do you? So I sometimes get called David Adams and I hate it. Nearly as much as when they call Joe, Joe Newman. Maybe it's best to keep them guessing. Like I said, it's confusing . . . and we're just the part of the Family who live here.

So, like I said, Mam had been flapping about like a demented mongoose for days now doing a lot of yelling at me. And no, I don't actually know what a demented mongoose does because I haven't actually met one but since they're always telling me to use my imagination, I am doing. And that's what I think she's like. And it's always me that gets yelled at. And finally today's the day, and there's a strange smell in the air, like polish. And things are looking pretty shiny. Even us. The piano is gleaming. I just hope nobody (like Dad) puts a cup down on it.

It's only 9am and Pete's already had two beers. The buffet for tea has been raided . . . or maybe just tampered with, and Joe who's eleven and just three months younger than me is drunk because he's been "tasting" the punch. Mam's walking around still tidying and straightening things, and me and Peter are feeling a bit yucky because we've been eating our selection boxes since 6am and playing on my computer. I don't know why Mam doesn't just leave things as they always are – messy. After all, what's the point when as soon as people come they'll make a mess of things again?

What you have to understand here is that my Mam is the sort of mam that never cooks, because she says it's a waste of time because people just eat it. So why doesn't she feel the same about cleaning? Usually she does and

Pete never notices anyway. Grandma says they're both "as bad as each other", whatever that's supposed to mean. But Grandma says "keev" instead of kiev and a few other strange words. She says "drownded" when she means "drowned" but "drownded" does exist. I know. I looked it up in the dictionary to prove to Grandma that it didn't and it did. So I used it at school at the Scrabble club and they tried to disallow it. You should have seen their faces when it was in the dictionary. Anyway, Mam and Pete never throw anything away. They sort of collect things. In case they come in handy. And they're always economising. That means that they never buy anything unless it has a reduced sticker on and if it has, they buy it ... even if none of us like it. Grandma once bought twenty-four jars of pickled onions because they were only ten pence a jar and a lady in the queue asked Grandad what they tasted like. He had to tell her he didn't know because none of us like pickled onions and she went off to join another queue even though it was longer. We're really good at history in our house because we spend so much time reading dates and checking which century things come from. Like cans of things. By the time they get a reduced sticker you see, they're usually past their sell-by date. Mam and Pete are weird really. It's like when they buy us something (like a work book of maths) that we never wanted or asked for anyway, they think we should be pleased about it and then they complain if we don't cherish and look after the thing we never wanted. It's like the tidying up. Why do we have to tidy our rooms up and put stuff away when they don't tidy their room? They leave books and newspapers all over the floor ... but guess what? That's right – we're not allowed to. If I question Mam and tell her all the junk should be sorted and chucked out, she tells me it's not hers, it's Pete's. And if I ask him and tell him to get rid of some of the old-fashioned stuff, he ignores me. He touches his "ban the bomb" medal that he always wears around his neck, like he's frightened it'll disappear, and offers to let me listen to his Joan Baez tapes. Again. Then he says to look at the Beatles and aren't I pleased he kept all their old records and I don't dare tell him, "No, I'd rather have the new CDs."

I bet in the olden days parents were tidy and mams and dads lived together with their kids. Their own kids, that is, so the kids were with their own mams and dads. Now everybody seems to live together with a mam and dad maybe but you can never tell who belongs to who and that's another problem. Mam says that people don't own people . . . but I think she forgets that when it comes to me. If she doesn't think she owns me she certainly acts like she does. Huh.

Anyway here we are ready and waiting for The Invasion. Me and Joe play at guess the identity . . . and that's just with the ones who are supposed to be relations but we're not quite sure whose. Then there's the other odd thing. Guests always seem to come to our house in twos. Like maybe they need protection from us or they think it's a couples only party or we're recruiting for Noah's Ark. Maybe it's to do with school and always being told "Get into twos and form a crocodile." I never understood that bit and I still don't. Why do a class of children all in twos and holding hands look like a crocodile? Maybe it's their teeth. All that forced brushing first thing in the morning and last thing at night.

Dad and Diane arrive first. They tumble through the door covered in snow but with great orange suntans. Dad's wearing three hundred pullovers and probably hoping for a three hundred and first as a prezzie from us and Diane is wearing a crop top and tight trousers. She looks dead trendy but frozen. Even with the suntan. They've just been to Jamaica, you see. They live in Edinburgh now and Dad can only come down to see me if Diane drives because he never has any money for the bus fare. Maybe they walked to Jamaica. He passes me a present but says he would like to borrow it and that's before I've opened it. It's a Swiss army knife. I love it, Dad loves it (his got stolen by the bailiffs who came to his last flat), I just know Mam will hate it. Not only will she not trust me with it but she'll not trust Dad with it and she'll blame Diane for letting us get our hands on it. If I know my mam she'll confiscate it like she did my nail clippers with the Loch Ness Monster picture on. (In case I did something dangerous with it like clip my toenails.) She's strange, my mam.

Next there's Uncle Brian and Hazel and The Pests, Holly and Ashley, two little girl pests who follow me about and want to hold my hand all the time and eat things that they chew and chew and chew and then sneeze out of their mouths and noses (at the same time!) all over the wall. They're nearly as bad as the posh relatives I don't know who want to hug and kiss me. Mind, that does have its good points because they hug me and say "Haven't you grown?" and then they pass me a pound coin like it's a reward for growing. There's a lot of money to be made in growing. I asked Dad once why grown-ups gave you presents for growing and he said he didn't know but would I make sure everyone knew that he's grown lately. I had to keep walking by his side saying "Eee Dad, aren't you getting big . . .?" but all that happened was people kept telling him he should give up the drink then he'd lose weight. I don't think he liked that much.

Now, Uncle Brian isn't a real uncle; he's an adopted one because of Mam. I have a lot of adopted relatives and it's really weird because I can't tell how many cousins I've got. There are some that are real cousins but I'm never sure which.

Then there's Pete's lot. They're different to our lot because they talk posh. There's Connie first of all who Mam would have me call Grandma Connie but Connie says to call her Connie and she's Pete's mam, and Joe and Peter's grandma. That much is fine. Connie spends her time trying to improve our minds by buying Mensa books whilst my grandma spends her time trying to improve our appearance by ironing our clothes. I asked Mam why it was that we get dressed up to go to Connie's house and don't bother when we go to my grandma's. She said something about "horses for courses . . ." and I suppose my grandma does love the horse racing but I don't know what that has to do with clothes. I don't know which is worse.

By now there's Auntie Anne, my godmother, and Uncle Ray who was Dad's best man when he (Dad) married Mam and he's Auntie Anne's husband and not a real uncle at all. So Jennifer and Jonathan (other pests) aren't real cousins even though they are Uncle Ray's kids, and Uncle Brian (who's not a real uncle, like I said) is Jennifer's godfather. Hazel is Brian's girlfriend and Holly and Ashley's (major pests) mam. I like Hazel. She's normal. I think she has bother knowing who people are. Diane is Dad's wife. (Now.)

Then there's Uncle Joe who has Gem. He is Joe and Peter's sort of uncle because he was married to their mam's sister but she was married to someone else before. But anyway, we all love Gem because he's a dog and less complicated and he doesn't pretend to be related to anybody, he's just a dog. He barks and wees a lot. And steals biscuits. At least he doesn't sneeze them all over the room.

So you can see that we don't really fit the sort of thing you find in books. I mean, if we had a story written about us there would have to be a sort of guide in the front of the book explaining who each person was. Then there's the strange behaviour. Mam's sort of on guard. She's watching that Dad doesn't throw his cigarette end into the gas fire. It's one of them that look like real coal but it's not. Last year we had real coal, you see, and Dad will forget. There's the Aga in the kitchen and she's frightened that the pests will burn their fingers on it but nobody takes any notice. Actually I heard her say to Gurcharn, her Indian friend who was Mam's bridesmaid when she married Dad, that little children were not a good idea in our house because of the Aga. The problem was that Gurcharn thought she'd said "the art work" and said she'd help her carry it upstairs. I think Mam thought Gurcharn was drunk because there was no way they could carry a 20 ton Aga upstairs so she just told her that she needed it for the sausage rolls. Gurcharn looked really confused. But then people do look confused when they talk to my mam. Then she keeps checking to see that Pete is still upright. He only drinks at weekends you see and sometimes he falls asleep on the settee. I don't suppose it would matter if he did that today really. Not that he'll get much chance. Dad's getting the guitar and I see an opportunity to earn a bit of cash by bringing out the violin. Peter's blasting REM from his bedroom and as always Joe's got his telly on full blast. Then somebody says it's nearly three and what about the Queen?

Dad immediately bursts into song and a rather unusual version of Bohemian Rhapsody fills the air. Dad makes up the words as he goes along and Uncle Ray's got Mam's guitar now. One of the posh relatives who must be related to somebody somehow wants to hear the Queen's speech, Dad's singing Queen, Joe's just located the Greatest Hits Album and Uncle Ray's singing "Streets of London" . . . This is probably a good time for me to bring through the electric guitar and amplifier.

I glance at Mam. She's sitting down and the sloe gin

185

bottle is beside her. This is not a good sign. My Mam doesn't often drink so she's not very good at it. She'll be OK while she's sitting down but once she starts to show people out and she gets near the fresh air that's when problems will begin. She'll fall over. I know. Also she'll start with the embarrassing tales. You see, with "Streets of London" I thought the bit in the second verse about "Carrying her home in two carrier bags" was about the old lady being carried home in two bags. You know, like she's in bits? It was a mistake, I know that, but not as big a mistake as telling Mam, because although she explained to me that it meant carrying her "home" . . . like her house . . . that was all her worldly goods, so to speak . . . she's never stopped telling people about it and I feel a right dip.

Mam took me to a barbecue once when I was just little and Uncle Ian (another adopted uncle, my godfather) had to drive us home. He even put me to bed. He mustn't have been able to find my pyjamas and I woke up next morning wearing a track suit. I looked more like I'd been training all night than sleeping. Then there was the other time that Uncle Ray babysat and decided that I was too old to take my bedtime drink from a feeding bottle. He took the teat off the top of the bottle and seemed to expect me to swig back my milk like brown ale. So you can see I've always had a hard time with my Mam.

Anyway, it's 11pm now and people are starting to go. I did try to go to bed but there seems to be a party of strangers discussing nappies in my bedroom. I don't think they're related to anybody at all. They're gatecrashers, I reckon, who've just come in off the street. So much for a Christmas Family Gathering. Next year I think I'll go to President Clinton's White House. I expect I'll know just as many people.

Samuel Khanna (15)

*My Collected Stories

These are a collection of the stories that have happened to me. Please note that all of these are completely true.

My Uncle David

My Uncle David and the Bull
My uncle David was born and brought up in London, educated in a public school, and had never been slightly close to Manchester before he was 30 years old. When he was 30 he decided to sell everything and move to a farm in Scotland. He is a big man, over 6 foot 4 inches. He had just come into some money, so he bought a small farm in the middle of nowhere. He bought some sheep and a Jersey cow, and a bull with the farm. The locals thought that he wouldn't last seven months; he did in fact last seven years plus.

In our family we have Christmas lunch at our house, and our uncle David and his family are invited. After we have had our meal we sit and talk about how we are and what has happened. Many old memories come up. This one Christmas lunch, we asked him what ever did happen to the bull? He said that the bull became very ill, so he called the vet out. The vet said that the bull couldn't fart and that it would die from its stomach popping unless he could get the air out of it. Uncle David asked how he could do that. The vet said he would need to shove a hose down its throat.

The local farmers came over to help, all twelve of them, and they tried for hours and hours. I must just mention that a bull is an enormous thing and that if it didn't want

187

to move not even a JCB could get it to move. Each time a farmer grabbed the bull's head, he hit the wall of the barn with extreme force about 0.01 seconds later. The bull just flicked its head and off flew the farmer. After hours of trying they finally got the hose down the bull's throat. The vet said that David would have to do this every day for the rest of the bull's life and he asked David if he would like him to put it down. David said no and that he would shove it down the bull's throat.

You may wonder why they didn't use a sedative; well, by this time the bull was rather old and the vet said that the bull might not wake up if he darted it. All the farmers had a bet that the bull would be dead in two weeks' time.

The bull did in fact live for another two years, with David daily shoving the hose down the bull's throat on his own. The bull did later die when it got lost and stuck in a bog.

Then in an inquisitive sort of a way I asked what he had done with the bull. He said, "Buried it, of course." This bull must have weighed over a tonne. So I asked him where. It turned out that he had got the tractor and pulled the bull to a nice spot with a view of the whole farm and started digging. When he was halfway through digging this hole 8 foot deep and 8 foot wide, he had to dash off for the Dalmaly games (no forward planning, like my father). This is like the highland games for Dalmaly. When he got back, the bull and the tractor had sunk three foot into the marsh land they were on. So he spent the rest of the day digging the tractor out.

While he had been burying the bull, the rest of the cows came round; he said he thought that they were paying their last respects. We think that they were saying "What a fool, why doesn't he send it to the knackers' like everyone else does?"

We all sat round the table in total disbelief; like the

cows we asked him why had he not sent it to the knackers' like normal farmers do. He said, "Well, the bull had been on the farm all its life so I thought that it should be buried there."

My Uncle David, Sheep Saver Extraordinaire

My uncle David let his sheep out on the mountains for most of the year. Twice a year he rounded them up at dipping time and shearing time. When it was time for either of these my uncle David and the rest of the shepherds would go out on the mountain collecting up the sheep. One of the dogs scared a mother sheep into a loch. A loch is like a lake; it is very close to freezing point and is very deep. All the baby sheep followed the mother in. Normally when sheep fall into lochs they die, because the water slowly seeps into their coat, and the weight drags them down. None of the shepherds could swim so they normally just let the sheep drown. Not my uncle David. He jumps in and swims out to the sheep, turns the sheep over and life-saves it back to land; all the lambs followed swimming back. The shepherds thought that David was mad, but they bought him a number of whiskies down the local pub for being so brave. When you realise that a sheep is worth only about £5, his action must have seemed so crazy. He had risked hypothermia, frostbite and possible drowning, for less than the price of a bottle of whisky.

My Dad

"The Grey-Haired Old 'Git'."

Before I start this section I must tell you a little about my dad. For a start, he is very accident-prone. This is not due to bad luck, but the fact he is without the forward planning of a five-year-old child. Most normal people when they see burglars coming out of a house go and dial 999. Not my dad. He has to chase after them for a mile trying to make a citizen's arrest, and then when he has caught one of them sit on him shouting, "I am making a citizen's arrest." Which was met with many expletives as you can imagine. Then the mate of the boy being sat on came over to him, saying, "If you don't get off him, I'll bash your head in."

So he got off the boy, but after that most sane human beings would have gone home and called the police. Not my dad. He carried on chasing them until they got on a train. Even then he wasn't happy to end it there. My dad demanded that they stopped the train at Harrow train station and search it for them. The underground worker said that he had to have the police permission to do so, so my dad ran all the way to the police station to try to get them to stop the train. I don't know what happened after that, all I know is that he didn't get the train stopped and the thieves got away.

Everyone at home thought that he had gone to get a paper, so when he reappeared two hours later, there was a mental block between us and him, because he thought we had seen him run off after the crooks. We asked him where he had been, and when he said "to the police station" we were all completely shocked.

So where do we get the phrase "Grey-Haired Old *Git*"? Well, later on that evening my sister went into the pub and overheard two boys talking about a "grey-haired old git", chasing their friends through a park. My sister was too embarrassed to admit that it was her dad. She got home and told us about it, and that is what we have called him since then.

My Dad and the Wasps' Nest

Yet again a section with animals in and these ones were really mad, not mad as in stupid, but mad as in very, very, angry. Now what would you do if you had a wasps' nest in your garden? Same as me, call the exterminator. Not my dad, he goes out and starts poking the nest with an eight-foot long wooden pole. That was not a good idea. Not happy with angering a whole nest of wasps so that they fly all over the garden trying to sting anything that moves, he then decides to get a Hoover and suck up the wasps.

This was an even worse idea. He got the Hoover and went to the nest. This did suck up half the wasps, but what he didn't realise was that there was a way out and when several thousand irate wasps appeared behind him, boy was he in trouble. What made matters worse was that he by this time had moved the Hoover over to the other side of the garden. Now there were several thousand extremely angry wasps frantically flying across the garden, one of which locked on to my dad, and started chasing him round the garden. He ran inside and flung off his jumper shouting, "There's one down my back." The jumper was removed with such force that an ornamental wall plate flew across the room, and smashed on the floor next to me.

We were all in fits of laughter for the next twenty minutes. My dad said that it wasn't funny and he could have been seriously stung. We said that it was his own fault and he shouldn't be so stupid in the future. He was vindicated though, as the wasps decided that living in our garden wasn't worth the hassle. They packed up home and had moved by the next morning, never to return.

Angharad Guy (5)

*The Big Master

The big master lives
where the big children go,
down the steps, through the door,
if you see the telephone
that's his house.

Charlotte Cropper (9)

The big master
is all different colours clothes.
He's got a jacket and a tie,
and trousers, socks and shoes.

All day he just works:
he does writing.
He goes to his friend's house
to get more paper.

He goes home with the girl miss
because he lives with her.
She's got a daughter,
and they go shopping every day.

The miss has a new car,
a big one, it's black,
she crashed the little one.

The big master is a bit nice
and a bit nasty.
The naughty boys get
sent to see the big master.

TURNING ROUND THE LABYRINTH

Susannah Garrard (9)

Edward Goodacre (8)

*The Promise to Balder

I swear, said the wolf,
Shaking and gnashing his teeth.

I swear, said the hawk,
Roosting on the cliff.

I swear, said the berry,
Oozing its juice.

I swear, said the axe,
Red hot from the forge.

I swear, said the gold,
Molten from the mould.

I swear, said the dagger,
Blazing in the sunlight.

Christopher Meek (12)

Edward Goodacre (8)

*Theseus and the Minotaur

I tied the thread
To the door,

Unravelling the ribbon,
Turning round the labyrinth

My hands feeling for fur
And the sharp point of horns,

Listening for his heart
Butting against his bruised bones.

Into the nub of the puzzle!
The eyes of the beast

Staring in the forgotten dark.
I leapt at his neck,

My arms tight round him.
He was going mad,

Banging and thumping.
I strangled him.

I looked for the ball of string
And wound myself out.

I was a hero.

Elizabeth Roy (16)

Elizabeth Roy (16)

*Rescue

"Mark! Welcome home!"

Mark King looked up from shutting the gate and saw his foster-mother smiling at him from the veranda. He felt his depression lighten briefly, although the sight was unremarkable: a conventional welcome, and the house which with its white weatherboarding and green tin roof could have been any of a thousand in outback New Zealand. But Rachel seemed as untroubled by his unannounced arrival as she had been twelve years ago when he had first come to Urewera, bewildered and cold with pain, clutching a suitcase that dragged and banged against his legs, and thrust her into the unaccustomed rôle. Her simple acceptance of this and him had been the first thing to reach him; yet with the acceptance she maintained a shrewd knowledge of his moods, a concern for his welfare, and a right to ask questions. So when they were seated in the back living room she said inevitably, "Something's wrong, isn't it?"

Mark sat staring at his hands; hands that were tanned, but given his Maori blood not as brown as might have been expected; a craftsman's hands. He knew she did not fully expect an answer, and for that very reason felt somehow obliged to give her one, only he couldn't see past the fog of tiredness and discouragement to coherent thought.

"It helps to talk about it sometimes," she said. "Honestly." But he still hesitated, partly because he was not at all sure he agreed, and partly because he was always uncertain in communication. Finally he blurted out helplessly, "You know I'm out of a job?"

"But how? The Institute can't have thrown you out, not after—"

"They didn't; I left."

Rachel looked at him. "Why, Mark?"

"Things." He took a deep breath, and looked up at her. "I left a year ago. I'm sick of the place. All arty students making Genuine Maori Crafts, and no one who . . . no one who *cares*." He added bitterly, "I'll bet all their fathers encouraged them to learn."

"Mark—"

"I hate it there. They don't even have proper tools. Would you believe, Rachel, the number of people who call themselves carvers, who've never even heard of the adze – or only seen it in museums? I know if I had the adze I'd be able to do – I don't know, *something*. But there's no

199

one who knows enough to teach me – no one. I've hitch-hiked over the whole blasted country, and there's no one." His mouth twisted. "So now I go back to the Institute, and apologise nicely, and carry on trying to teach idiots which end of a chisel's which. Wouldn't Dad laugh if he knew?"

"Mark!"

"Well, wouldn't he?"

"Mark," Rachel said impatiently, "what does your father have to do with this? That was twelve years ago, for goodness' sake. He's miles away now. When will you stop killing yourself about what happened? The sooner you – Mark!"

Mark had swung away to the back door which was open on to the veranda. Before him climbed the dark green bush, split by the zig-zagging fire breaks, orange ribbons laced around the bulk of the hill. But he didn't see that, nor did he hear the cries of the birds, or the far-off shouts of the farm hands. He saw a face, fair-haired and lightly freckled with the sun, set coldly as it turned its back on the half-caste son who was a constant embarrassment because he chose to acknowledge his Maori heritage, and whose obsession was to study at the Institute of Maori Arts and Crafts in Rotorua. Dad had doubtless found it a relief to escape back to England, leaving his dead wife, a country he had always hated even though she loved it, and the embarrassing Maori son behind.

Mark turned his back on the face and brushed past Rachel. But at the door he looked back. "Don't worry over me," he said, and then went out.

The next morning Mark came downstairs feeling unaccountably wary and taut, and was reassured and relieved to find that Rachel, with her usual serenity, calmly ignored anything that had happened the previous day and was glowing at the prospect of a new one. After breakfast she asked him if he would return a book to a neighbour for her. "Though 'neighbour' isn't exactly the right word. You don't know Eru Wirihana, do you? Very solitary, lives way up in the bush, and if people want to talk to him they can toil up the hill. What you might call a Maori with a chip, although I'm not sure he doesn't pretend to be more racist than he is. As far as he's concerned, the whites have done nothing that the Maoris couldn't or haven't done better."

"They haven't," Mark said. Rachel looked at him quickly, then laughed.

"You ought to get on well together. As a matter of fact, now I come to think of it, he's a retired—"

But just then one of the men who helped on the farm came in, and Rachel never finished the sentence. She gave him the book with the instructions "straight up the fire-break and turn right when you come to a path. You'll see the house from there", and Mark went.

It was another hot, dry day – Rachel said that there had been little rain for weeks – but it was cooler up among the bush. He climbed the firebreak, a forty-foot wide sandy track to prevent danger spreading in a bushfire, and felt the tension blow away again like the little puffs of loose dust and sand raised by his feet. He had always loved it up here, where his child mind had half feared, half exulted in the taniwhas he imagined hiding behind the thrusting tree ferns. A taniwha was a water creature, but there was always the chance one might have escaped, hungry, and wild . . . He smiled indulgently at the memory, but even so felt something of the old excitement as he turned down the first break in the bush that might be called a path.

But there was no taniwha. There was only a giant pohu-tukawa tree surging above the house at its roots. The house was made of logs, so mossy and faded that it gave the impression of having grown rather than been built, and the corrugated iron roof sat incongruously and self-consciously in its peeling and blistered paint. The scuffed door was propped half open, and when Mark knocked he heard a rough command to enter.

It was dark inside, for there was only one dusty window through which the thick green light of the underbush slanted; even the open door contributed little.

"Who're you?"

Mark turned to face the voice, and as he moved light slipped in past his shoulder. Several gleaming eyes flashed at him suddenly, darkening the instant he started and cut off the beam of light.

"Cat got your tongue?"

This time Mark, his eyes becoming adjusted to the dimness, saw a seated figure in the farthest corner of the hut. The old Maori sprawled awkwardly, with one leg on the seat of another chair, and two crutches leaning against it. Mark started to answer the question, but even as he delivered Rachel's message his eyes were deciphering the wall behind the old man, and he was stunned by what he saw. Running for the whole length of the wall, about three feet high, was an elaborately carved Maori lintel. Wooden monsters writhed among twisted wooden heroes, inlaid at intervals with circles of iridescent paua shell – the eyes that had startled him. Above the lintel hung two traditional Maori weapons: a taiaha, or carved wooden spear, ornamented with feathers and dog hair; and a greenstone club called a mere.

Eru Wirihana nodded as Mark finished, then twisted his head back to where Mark was still gazing in awe. "Well?" he said. "What's wrong, boy?"

"It's beautiful." Mark spoke softly, almost reverently.

The other raised an eyebrow. "Know anything 'bout carving?"

"Yes," Mark said quietly, still lost in the carving. "I teach – I used to teach at the Arts and Crafts Institute at

Rotorua." But he spoke absently, and ignoring manners moved over to examine it more closely. "Wherever did it come from?"

Eru snorted. "Come from? Huh. I made it, boy. All one piece, that is. Totara. There's those as says kauri's a better wood: it ain't."

"No," Mark said, scarcely listening as he bent forward to see the long, sweeping strokes. Then he straightened abruptly. "You said you *made* this? But – it must have been done with the adze – wasn't it?" He turned back to the unmistakable lines of the carving. "It must have been."

"Who's sayin' it weren't? Course I used an adze. Why not?"

"You know the adze?" Mark repeated blankly. "But – I – I looked everywhere. No one knows the adze any more. No one."

"Well, someone does," Eru said snappishly. "Why'd y' want someone who knows it anyhow? What do pakehas know about carving?"

The memory of yesterday still fresh in his mind, that stung. "I told you," he said tightly, "I used to teach at the Maori Institute. But I left, to try to find someone who could teach me the adze."

"Teach you!" the old man bellowed, abruptly furious. "You expect me to teach a tapu, a sacred Maori craft, t'a pakeha? A European? Never, you hear? Never!"

"I am not a pakeha!" Mark flung back, aware that this was not the way to respond, but unable to answer anything else. "My father was, but my mother and I are Tuhoe."

"I don't care if y'mother was Papa the earth mother," shouted Eru. "I'm of the Tuhoe tribe myself, an' I say I'll never teach a pakeha. Now get out!"

Mark snatched too late at control of his temper. "Mr

203

Wirihana, no one – Maori or pakeha – knows the adze any more, in the whole country, apart from you. If you don't teach me—"

"I told you, I'll never teach a pakeha. D'y understand? Never!"

"—if you don't teach me, Maori carving will die. Don't you care?"

"What does a pakeha like you care that Maori art's dyin', huh? An' anyway, if a pakeha's its only hope, it ain't dyin', it's already dead!"

There was nothing more to say, and Mark did not waste time saying it. He turned on his heel and walked out.

The following days were almost unendurable. To have actually found a carver who knew the adze – and not only knew it, was clearly a master of the craft – and to be denied teaching – for being a pakeha! Mark laughed bitterly, wondering what Dad would make of that one. By a week after the quarrel Rachel had soothed the worst of his pain, but he still lay awake that night, staring out of the window. The moon was full, and there was an extra glow in the sky, a sort of flickering reddish light. As though, he thought, the red-haired patupaiarehe, the fairies, were dancing through the night.

He turned over on his side, trying to relax, then suddenly sat up sharply.

Red light.

He was out of bed and staring out of the window, then flung himself down the stairs. He went straight to Rachel's room, threw open the door, and switched on the light. Ignoring her startled and blinking face he went over to her window, which unlike his faced towards the hill. Flinging back the curtains he cast one quick glance out and said abruptly, "Bushfire, up by Mr Wirihana's house. He's got a bad leg; I'm going."

Rachel came awake slowly. "Mark!"

"I'm going," he repeated. "Will you phone?"

"Yes, of course," Rachel said, sleepy but fully awake. "Go!" Mark went.

Outside, the wind was strong and cold, which seemed all wrong. His hair blew into his eyes, and the old coat he had pulled on over his pyjamas flapped and billowed, slowing him down. He stumbled, and the full buckets he carried slopped over, freezing against his skin, soaking his clothes. I'm going towards a fire, he thought, and I'm cold. Well, not for long. Already he could hear a faint snapping sound above the rush of the wind.

The firebreak was dry and sandy, Rachel said because there had been no rain ... The ground was steeper, he stumbled again. Then, quite suddenly, he could see the fire. On Eru Wirihana's side of the firebreak.

He choked, whether with the smoke or something else he never knew. He stopped to tie his handkerchief, soaked in water, over his mouth and nose, and then went on, towards the raging fire.

He came to the path, but here the fire was on both sides of the track, the trees blazing fiercely. He gripped the buckets so tightly that the metal handles cut into his palms; he could not tell if it was sweat trickling down his fists, or blood. I can't go down there, he thought wildly, looking down to Eru's house where the great pohutukawa tree blossomed brilliant scarlet as if in flower. I can't, not for him, I can't ...

Eru's words beat back at him furiously: "How much does a pakeha like you care that Maori art's dyin', huh?" Mark saw his father's face for an instant in that last, painfully melodramatic quarrel; "For all I care you can stay here with your stupid carving; I'm going back to England – with or without you!"; heard his own ten-year-old voice shouting violently "Go then! I wish you would,

I *hate* you"; heard himself a week ago not answering Eru, and the next instant was running down the flaming avenue, trying not to draw breath, trying to still the insistent questions . . .

His shoulder crashed into the door and it gave way, sending him stumbling into the room. But the sight of Eru stopped him short, coughing and choking with the smoke. The old Maori was sitting in his chair, his bad leg twisted under it, and his crutches sprawled away on the other side of the room. Since he couldn't escape to safety he would die with dignity and like a Tuhoe warrior. The flames outside in the night sky sent fantastic shadows wheeling round the room, and the light danced over the Maori spear and greenstone club which he held proudly in his hands.

Fiddling while Rome burned, Mark thought, just wasn't in it.

A soft polishing cloth lay on the floor near by; Mark grabbed it, soaked it, and thrust it at the old man.

Eru made no move.

Mark came closer to swearing then than any other time in his life. He reached out, knocked Eru's hands away, and tied the cloth over his mouth and nose. Then he put an arm round the other's shoulders and began trying to lift him. Eru said something about a warrior, muffled by the cloth, and Mark shouted back, "Warriors! All you ever think about is dying, isn't it, and how to die? How about trying to live for a change?" and heaved him up from his chair. The heat drove him back the first time he went near the door, but Mark set his teeth, dragged Eru through, and began to stumble as fast as he could towards the safety of the firebreak and untouched bush, Eru limp and unresisting in his arm.

*

Mark followed a vague nurse down a corridor, still seeing and hearing and smelling the fire in the white walls and floor and the clinical, antiseptic odour inseparable from hospitals. But he hardly noticed it – he had enough to worry about, just now.

The nurse opened a door and drifted aside, murmuring something indistinct about not being long, then faded away. Mark stood for a moment in the doorway, then went in, letting the door close behind him.

Eru lay with his eyes closed, and did not turn his head or even open them when Mark came in. But after a short, sharp silence he muttered, "Sid down."

Mark sat.

There was another silence. Then Eru said, "Why'd you come?"

"I thought you'd want to know what happened."

"Huh."

Mark waited, and after a moment Eru cleared his throat. "You've – you've bin back, then?"

Mark nodded. Eru cleared his throat again. "What's – how bad's the . . ." his voice died.

"The roof fell in," Mark said, though he knew Eru wasn't asking about the house. "The window was broken, and a lot of the furniture's damaged." He saw Eru open his mouth again, and added, as if reporting a death, "The lintel caught – but it could be restored, I think." He looked away quickly from Eru's face.

"You wantin' the job?" Eru demanded harshly.

Mark felt his temper rise. "No," he said. "It would take an expert."

"Thought you were one? Teacher at th' Institute of Maori Arts . . ."

"That," said Mark evenly, "doesn't make me an expert, and it certainly doesn't qualify me to restore your lintel. It would need to be restored using an adze, and I can't."

Eru opened his eyes sharply. "So that's why y'came," he said. "Since y' saved m'life I have to teach y' th'adze, eh? Might've known."

Mark clamped his mouth shut, and Eru shifted on the pillows. "Well?"

"Well what?"

"Said all you come to say, an't you? So now you can go home. Or d'you expect me t'thank you for saving my life?"

"No." Mark got up. "Knowing you" – but they had only met three times, he realised – "knowing you, I didn't expect thanks. Nor, you might like to know, did I come here expecting you to teach me the adze in gratitude. I don't want your gratitude any more than you want to give it." He turned to go, and was halfway to the door before Eru let himself speak.

"Boy . . ."

"Yes?" Mark looked back. Eru studied him for a few minutes, judging him.

"Somethin' y'said before." Eru coughed. "That y' couldn't find anyone else who knew th'adze in th' whole country."

"Yes?"

"Looks like my lintel won't be mended then, don't it?"

Mark looked at him impatiently. "Well, you'll have to do it yourself then, won't you?"

Eru lifted one bandaged hand. "Ae, looks like it," he said sarcastically. "Hold th'adze in m'teeth, I suppose."

"But – it will heal, won't it? I mean – you will be able to carve again?"

"Who said I couldn't?" Eru snapped, then recovered himself. "Don't know I want to wait that long, though. Looks like I'll have t'get someone t'do it for me. An' I reckon if it has t'be someone else, I'd rather they were Tuhoe than not."

"Yes?" Mark said again.

" 'Yes?' " Eru repeated violently. "Give me patience, boy! What else d'you want me t'say? D'you want th'job or not?"

Mark came back to the bed, staring at him. "Do you really mean that?" he asked unbelievingly.

"Course I do. I said it, didn' I? An' if," he added, "you're goin' t'tell me y'can't use an adze again, I'll – well, what is it?"

"It's not that," Mark said, his mind awhirl, but clutching at the most important thought. "It's – you said you'd rather it was a Tuhoe that restored the lintel. Well – on the night of the fire I found out – well, that I'm not."

"You're not a Tuhoe? When you shouted y'rself blue in face tellin' me y'were, not a week ago? An' now," he said witheringly, "I suppose you're goin' t'tell me you're not a pakeha either. What's that make you then?"

Mark grinned suddenly. "A New Zealander," he said. "Just another Kiwi."

Eru looked at him, then repeated unevenly, "Just another Kiwi." He choked suddenly, and started coughing helplessly. He leant back against the pillows, still coughing, but calmed eventually. "Just another Kiwi," he said again. "Ae. Y'know, if y'put two halves together y'd be surprised how often y'get a whole. Y'd be surprised."

Timothy Roe (8)

*The Magic Stick

Chapter One
One day when I was young I was walking in the woods when I came across a man standing by the path.

The path was steep and I was bending my back. So the man said, "Would you like this stick?" I said, "Yes please". The man handed the stick over. "Thanks," I said. The stick was just right for me. I carried on going up the hill. The stick made it much easier.

And somehow that stick has always been just right for me. So I suspect it grows!

Chapter Two
One day years later when I was grown up I was walking in the hills. I saw an old man standing by the path. The man could not climb the hill. I said, "Would you like my stick?" The man said "Oh, yes please." So I handed him the stick. "Thanks," he said. "It will help me a lot. I am really grateful. I have been waiting a long time for it."

When I got home I wondered what had taken place that day. It was all very strange.

Amy Carr (9)

*Circe and the Swine

I saw the enchantress
Tapping my crew
With a wand
That fell like a
Stalk of corn
Upon their
Gullible heads.

I hid an anemone
Under my tongue.
When I ate the bread
And honey and wine
I tucked it
Into the cave
Of my cheek.

Alastair Stewart (12)

Karim Bouzerda-Khan (7)

The Black Stallion

A long time ago there was this horse, called Artax, who lived in the Sahara. And he had a little stable which was owned by an old man. The black stallion had a lot of fun with the old man and his grandson. This boy's name was Amad. The grandfather's name was Muneer.

One day Amad was riding on his grandfather's horse,

the black stallion. He rode all the way through the desert until he got to a forest. He saw the sun going away quicker than it normally does. And then the moon came up. He looked up into the sky and suddenly he saw the moon.

Then he heard a noise. It was wolves howling. His horse got so scared it flew up in the air and landed on two feet and quickly landed on its two other feet. Then Amad fell off but he was still holding those nice soft leather reins. One of his legs was still in the stirrup. So he held on very tight to the reins that his grandma made, and pulling on his foot he freed it. He fell on his feet and nearly fell down.

The black stallion stopped and let Amad climb on his back. Then they galloped away. In the forest there was a bridge. On the left side there was water and on the right side there was water and lots of trees. The bridge was made of wood, bits of it were very thin and were not stuck together with nails. The black stallion stepped on them and then all the pieces of wood broke and the black stallion fell into deep water with Amad on his back. Only Amad's face was out of the water. Then he let go the reins with one hand and put his free hand on the fat strong pieces of wood on the bridge. So he was able to pull himself up. Then Amad had an idea. He rushed to one side of the river and called his horse. "Come on Artax, come on Artax, come on, good boy, come here boy!" And the black stallion swam to shore. Then they were back together again. Amad got on the horse and galloped away.

In the middle of the forest there were two trees and men hiding behind the trees. Then the men caught Amad. They tied him to a tree and wanted to steal the black stallion. They dragged the black stallion to the fort of their chief. Then Amad remembered that he had his knife. He managed to pull it out of his pocket and he cut the ropes. It seemed like ages but it wasn't.

Amad was searching everywhere. In an hour he found the fort. People were going into the fort and Amad was quite close so he rushed as quick as his feet could run. Finally he was in the fort. Then Amad heard some people coming so he hid behind an armoured statue. Then tiptoeing he sneaked behind the guards and found Artax.

Then he found the keys and he freed the black stallion. They rode out of the castle. They found themselves in a big black forest which was very spooky. And then Artax heard a bat. The bat flew past the horse very quickly so Artax ran and ran and ran and ran and ran.

Then he heard an owl, hou hou hou. The black stallion ran and ran and ran. Then he heard a big eagle and he ran and ran and ran. Then he started getting tired. He heard another bat. The bat went oua oua oua. Amad said: "Slow down boy!" The black stallion was so tired and Amad was so sleepy that he fell off his horse. Both of them slept there.

In the morning Amad woke up and he looked around the place because he couldn't remember where he was. Then he said: "Now I remember where I am. Artax, Artax! Come here!" The black stallion came. "Let's find some food," said Amad. They both rode away. They rode deeper into the forest. They saw a tree with lots of bananas. An old man came in front of Amad and Artax. He said: "Do you know how these woods are in the night?"

"No," said Amad to the old man. Then the old man said everything. "In the night the woods are bright. When you breathe you might see the black owl who is mean and nasty. He eats any children or horses in the forest. He is huge and fat. He might see you in the trees. He might flap down and eat you. You might be some bones just like me. If you do see him he will be black and red and white; behind his chest might be some frost." Then the old man stopped. Amad said: "What's your name, old man?"

"My name's Frost."

"Why did your mother and father call you Frost, Frost?"

"Because when I was a baby I was very cold. They felt that I was like ice. That's why they named me Frost."

Amad said: "Bye, Frost. See you soon, Frost, I think."

Then Amad went away galloping. He saw a tree house and got off the black stallion and tied the horse to a tree. Amad climbed up to the tree house. He saw the door and he went in. He saw spider webs and all just dust. There were lots of mice. Amad walked in. He looked everywhere. So if he found something he would keep it even if it was dusty. He doesn't mind because he has a feeling that he will find a river.

Then Amad found a handkerchief, then he found a chest. He pulled out the drawers of the chest and found a sleeping bag. Then he found a very dusty other one which had even bigger drawers and he looked in all the cupboards and found a tent.

Then on the roof he saw two bags, one was small, one was big. He put the tent and the sleeping bags in the big one. Then he looked at a spider web and he saw a little mouse stuck. But he was dead. "Poor little thing," he said.

It was starting to be night. Amad was walking with the black stallion. Then Amad said: "I hear something, I think it's an owl. Maybe it is the black owl."

He suddenly saw the black owl charging down at him from a big black old tree. As quick as a flash Amad took out his knife and pointed it at the black owl who was coming straight at him. The black owl was so close to Amad and he didn't realize that Amad had a knife and he didn't see Amad pointing the knife at him. The owl was so close to the knife that Amad killed him and the black owl fell straight to the ground. Blood was dripping from his heart. Amad put up the tent and got out the sleeping bag and went to sleep. Before he went to bed he tied the black stallion to a tree.

In the morning Amad woke up and said: "I think I want to have a bath." He went for a bath in a nearby waterfall but forgot to take the black stallion with him. A big black stink came; it was the dead owl's. Amad had forgotten to bury it. But a new black owl, who was very skinny, came out from the dead one. The black stallion went "Eh, eh, eh, eh!" Amad heard it and quickly came out of the waterfall and ran and ran even though he was naked. He saw the skinny black owl coming towards the black stallion, and Amad rushed forward, grabbed his knife and stabbed the skinny owl. Then he got dressed and took out his knife from the owl and buried them both. He got on the black stallion and rode away.

The black stallion was thirsty and Amad said: "Look over there, there's a river." They went to the river and drank and drank and drank. They were so full, they needed to do pee. Then they rode through the forest and the Sahara until they reached home before dark. His grandfather said: "You shouldn't go away without telling me."

"I would like to buy a new horse for you, grandfather," said Amad.

"OK," said his grandfather Muneer. "Should we buy the horse today?"

"Yes, Grandfather."

They went to the nearest horse-trader and bought a nice whitish horse with spots. Then they went home, and they put the horses in the stables. They went inside the house and Amad's grandfather Muneer went to the kitchen and brought out a huge tray of chicken and fruits and lemonade and they ate and ate and ate.

*Paradise Misplaced

Look here, Athena, snapped the Voice, *You know perfectly well you're not allowed to play the Joker until We say so.*

Athena tried to look sorry.

We hope you realise that as a result of your misbehaviour, the humans are now going to fade into the background.

"I *liked* the humans," Hera grumbled. "They were stupid."

"Come, my pet," Zeus said soothingly, "I'm sure you'll find some other amusing species. I'll make you one, if you like."

You know the Rules, Athena, They continued. *In fact you're quite intelligent for a Deity.*

Athena tried to look gratified.

What We don't understand is why you did it. The last time that happened, at the dawn of creation, the humans quite unexpectedly moved to the foreground. There We were, with a lovely new planet designed for fish, and Prometheus handed it over to the humans, the wastrel!

The Voice shook Their head. Well, They would have done if They had a head to shake.

It took a lot of time to turn them into educated idiots, but We managed it. The Voice was shaded with a hint of pride. *We did a good job of it too. Persuaded the humans to sell each other bits of paper that said they owned water.* Poseidon sniggered. Water shares had been his idea. *Going around paying people to pay them if they died. What was it called again?*

"Life insurance," interjected Hermes. He had invented that.

Then We created the masterstroke – politics. The art of lying truthfully. And they fell for it! There wasn't meant to be another Random move until after the humans had finished blowing themselves up. What are We to do with you?

"Send her to my planet," Ares suggested darkly.

"Send her to *my* planet," Hades suggested even more darkly.

"Send her to Daytime-TV Land," Hera hissed malevolently.

Surely her crime isn't that bad?

Everyone hastily shook their heads.

Exposure to banal trivia is still Our worst punishment?

Everyone nodded hurriedly.

Phew! Someone find out what the consequences are of Athena playing the Joker.

Ares stepped to the Holy Computer and keyed in a few digits.

"There is a 59% chance that the world will be handed over to another species, a 40% chance that the Elvis will return, and a 1% chance that nothing will happen."

Hmm ... We'll leave the Elvis option for the Millennium and go for the 1% chance. Commence.

Ares pressed a single key on the Sacred Keyboard.

Everything rippled. Waves of chance flooded Olympus. Probability trees sprouted up from the floor and shot through the ceiling. The gods fell to the floor. The Holy Computer shrieked hysterically and the Blessed Printer began to spew out reams of paper. Then, silence.

The gods looked around warily and got to their feet. Aphrodite giggled. Ares pulled a few probability twigs out of his hair and wrung drops of chance out of his tunic before hurrying to the Holy Computer.

"No!" he exclaimed, horrified.

What? the Voice demanded.

"It went for the 59% chance. There's going to be a power transfer."

The Voice didn't sit back. No doubt They would have sat back if They had anything to sit back *with*, but They didn't, so you'll have to use your imagination.

That's not exactly thrilling news, Athena. We hope you're sorry for all the trouble you've caused.

Athena tried to look contrite.

You'll just have to play the Joker again.

Athena tried to look aghast.

Yes, that's what We said. Play the Joker again. Someone unchain her.

A handful of nymphs stepped forward and released Athena. She straightened her helmet and rubbed her wrists to restore circulation.

Athena, come here, intoned the Voice.

Athena stumbled to the Throne of the Voice.

Kneel before Us.

"I can't. I've got pins and needles in my legs."

There was a frigid silence. The Voice drummed Their fingers on the Throne's armrests. In theory.

Fine. You won't kneel before the Mighty Voice because you've got pins and needles in your legs. Anything else you want to object to?

"Yes. I don't know where You got this helmet from, but it doesn't fit. And as for the chinstraps! They were out-dated in the days of flares! *No-one* wears—"

That's enough, Athena.

"But You said—"

THAT'S ENOUGH!

Athena regarded the billowing cloud the Voice occupied and wisely shut up.

Play the Joker again.

A lot of people have suggested that the gods spend their time playing dice to decide our fates. Some people even go as far as hypothesising that we are the game-pieces.

They are wrong.

The gods in actual fact play an intriguing card game known as Black-Jack. As for the theory that consequences are unpredictable, that's nonsense too. They use a second-hand PC35782/AFU40 which handles data very well, considering.

Athena and the other gods took their places at the Card table.

Play.

Hera put down the three of clubs. Housewives all over Belgium began to hit their husbands over the head with rolling pins.

Hades put down the three of hearts. A second-rate composer suddenly had a full-scale Requiem in his head *dying* to be written down.

Athena put down the Joker.

The Holy Computer Screen flickered. Ares leaned forwards, scanning the lists of figures intently.

"I knew we shouldn't have bought a second-hand model," he stated eventually. "No first-hand computer would do something so stupid—"

Ares, which option has it taken?

" . . . I told You that computer dealer was shifty. Even when the Holy Printer broke down and his emergency phone number didn't seem to exist, You wouldn't pay attention. I did warn You. But would You listen? *Oh* no. Just because You're omnipotent—"

Ares, which option has it taken?

" . . . If You'd made sure he was a registered salesman, none of this would have happened. Now we've got to put up with another species ruling the world."

The gods held their collective breath.

We don't think We heard you properly, Ares.

"I knew we shouldn't have bought a second-hand mod—"

220

No, not that bit.

"Now we've got to put up with another species ruling the world."

Which species?

"Human Women."

Hermes suddenly realised that he wouldn't be very good at carrying Divine messages to Belgian housewives hitting their spouses over the head with rolling pins, and Apollo muttered to a minor faun they'd have to start spreading those stupid legends all over again.

Human Women, the Voice repeated. Their tone brought a terrified hush to the Hall. *Ares, what would the consequences be if Athena were to play the Joker one final time?*

"I can't." Athena tried not to look smug.

What?

"I can't."

Is she being humorous?

"I can't play the Joker one last time because there are only two Jokers in the Deck."

That's absurd, sputtered the Voice. *Ridiculous – only two Jokers when there are four of everything else! Whose idea was that?*

"Um . . . Yours, actually."

Oh. The Voice subdued. Now that They thought about it, They did seem to recall saying some silly things in Their adolescent years. *When can you next play the Joker?*

"When the Deck finishes."

But that's—

"The end of an era."

We haven't got an era.

"I am aware of that fact."

We're running out of Time.

"I didn't create Time."

But you did create this conundrum!

Aphrodite sidled up to Zeus and tapped him winsomely. "What's a conununundrum?"

"Creating isn't the same as being responsible for," Athena said firmly. "*You* created Fate, Chance and Black-Jack. *They're* responsible for this conundrum. *I* just manipulated it."

Clever words aren't going to get you out of this, Athena, the Voice snarled. *If men are destroyed, you go with them.*

The silence in the hall was deafening. If someone had said they wanted to give up omniscience and take up fly-fishing instead, the silence couldn't have been louder.

In the early days of the pantheon, the Voice had been a giddy young Entity. They had declared several new Laws, such as *You wait hours for one and then three come along together so henceforth We shall work in threes* and *There can only be two Jokers in a deck of Cards.* Unfortunately, one of Their earlier Laws dictated that everything They said *must*, alas, come about.

By rashly threatening Athena, the Voice had unwarrantedly made a promise. And if Athena was killed, the rest of the gods would become mortal, theology would crash around the Voice's non-existent ears and paradox would become dead fashionable.

Us and Our big mouth . . . the Voice muttered.

"O Mighty Voice, I think I perceive a solution." Athena smiled inscrutably.

The Voice leaned forwards eagerly, a clever trick for a cloud.

Speak on, beloved subordinate.

"I'll need the Holy Computer for a while."

There was confused arguing in the background.

"Only a trained programmer can operate the Holy Computer!" Ares protested jealously.

"O Revered Brother, I have been attending PASCAL programming classes."

222

You haven't been mingling with mortals, have you?

"Well ... um ... there was this register going around ..."

Who did you sign yourself in as?

"Athena, daughter of Zeus. Is something wrong?" she added, as the Voice caused an unoffending tapestry to disappear in acrid smoke. "They couldn't have guessed who I was. I left Pooky at home."

But turned up in your armour?

"Mmm-hmm. The teacher said I looked familiar. Naturally; I founded the college."

And We suppose you told him that?

Athena blithely nodded. She had actually turned up in jeans and a Beatles T-shirt claiming to be Sally Whitfield. Still, what's wrong with a good wind-up every now and again, eh?

In that case, We're not surprised atheism is popular. Go ahead, do what you must.

Athena seated herself at the Sacred Keyboard and tapped away industriously, impervious to the rubbernecking behind her. Eventually, she rose declaring, "There, that should do it."

The assembled deities craned forwards as one body.

"I can't see anything!" Aphrodite piteously exclaimed.

"Of course you can't," Athena agreed. "The Holy Computer's been disconnected."

"Disconnected"?

"If we stuck to the rules which You, in Your ineffable wisdom, created, men would be utterly wiped out and my darling family would become mortal. This planet which we fought so hard to sustain would collapse into itself, victim of our folly."

We know all that. Save the epic speeches for the priests and prophets.

Athena looked injured. It had taken her mere minutes

to write the speech but centuries of waiting for the perfect moment to deliver it.

She raised her voice for dramatic effect. "If enough Cards are piled on top of the two Jokers, the effect will be less catastrophic and men will not be exterminated!"

Her technique enjoyed the same success as Hephaestus attempting a hundred-metre sprint.

"There'll be backlashes for decades!" Zeus protested.

We'll have to forfeit Our Plan to do that! wailed the Voice.

"I'm not giving up my go to cancel out the Jokers!" Apollo announced. "I've worked hard to ensure that Accrington Stanley win the cup this year."

"Precisely my point." Athena stroked Pooky's ruffled feathers. "Being selfish deities, none of you are willing to drop out of the Game for the good of man- or woman-kind."

In addition to being more self-centred than spinning tops, the majority of Olympian inhabitants were not on conversing terms with one another – further diminishing the likelihood of divine co-operation. The only person everyone was speaking to was the sandwich boy, and all he ever said was "Meat, fish or veg?"

"But brethren . . . sistren, I can prove to you that the sacrifice of your Cards is a worthy one indeed."

Oh yeah? How?

"I have travelled to Other."

Now for a philosophical discussion on Reality.

Reality is a probability tree. On one branch, you had eggs and bacon for breakfast; on the other, cereal. All these nanoscopic second-by-second choices mean nothing to you, but every single decision causes reality to fragment into the Other Places, the worlds which might have been.

Worlds with only the slightest of differences – grey socks as opposed to navy – flourish thickly together, intermingling. Worlds where Hitler left his speech notes at home prior to his first public appearance exist in the far reaches of the Other dimension. Hovering on the border of Nightmare with reinforced boundaries are the Other Places where slimy yellow blobs drop from the sky and things with tentacles instead of faces walk – er, crawl – the earth.

We all know about Other, Athena. The Voice was tinged with weariness. *What good is it if you tell us that the world will flourish under the rule of women if it turns out you trod the wrong reality?*

"She might lie!" Hermes growled. "She might say that women rule the world with prudence and care just to get her own way!"

There were mutterings of agreement from the more chauvinistic and misogynistic deities, i.e. everyone.

What have you to say to that, Athena?

Athena beamed sunnily. "I took a camcorder."

The thing about Athena was that she was antagonisingly practical. No other deity would think of replacing the Sanctified Owl of Logic and Common Sense with a stuffed owl called Pooky. Admittedly, "Pooky" was less of a mouthful and being stuffed, didn't dig septic talons into your shoulders, but the fact was inescapable – Athena was nauseating.

Athena produced a video from the recesses of her robes and shoved it into the Consecrated VCR.

The video began to roll, partly because Athena was a goddess and could effectuate things without uttering a word, but mostly because she had pressed "play" on the remote control.

Songs of Praise. Alanna Titchmarsh is reading from Genesis:

Then Goddess took the Wo-man She had created and from her ankle-bone formed a companion for the

225

Wo-man who was named Man to show how they were essentially the same but Wo-man would always have more than Man.

And She said unto Wo-man, "Behold, I have created Man from your ankle-bone. You will always be above him but must not tread on him too hard because he is fragile."

And the Wo-man was named "Eve", which means "Beginning", and the Man was named "Adam" which is a politely distorted version of "A Damn—". Eve never got to finish the sentence, though scholars have suggested that she was going to say "—Stupid Mistake, Creating Him."

An interview room. The candidate shifts uneasily in his chair. He's done everything he can to appear executive and feminine. The interviewers aren't fooled, but they are impressed. He is called Leslie, which will look acceptable on facsimiles.

The interviewers glance at each other.

A rub of stiletto heels – he might feel intimidated, the only man working at an executive level.

A toss of permed tresses – so what? We can claim we're equal opportunity employers.

A flutter of rainbow-hued eye-shadow and his fate is decided. Lipsticked seams ease themselves into business smiles.

The army.

"Move it, you bunch of *men*!" yells the CO, her lip curled in scorn.

The soldiers grit their teeth. *Men* indeed! Their eyes glitter with suppressed fury.

The bewildering volley of sounds and images were halted by Athena. Or rather, the remote control.

"There's more," she said quietly. "Suffragons instead of suffragettes; Black-Jill instead of Black-Jack; Hera's the Queen of Heaven—"

Zeus roused himself from his stunned stupor. "But Hera's the Queen of Heaven now!" he managed feebly.

"Ah, but this time she'll mean it. And you'll be her Consort."

"Does that mean I won't have to play hostess when those puny mortals come around to visit?" Hera asked eagerly, all joy and exultation.

"That's right."

Artemis looked up. "And I can put up as many shelves and fix as many food processors as I like?" she said.

Athena nodded benignly.

"But they're the ones who have to dust the shelves and use the food processors?"

"Yep."

"Great!"

"Mmm, but have you considered the drawbacks?"

"Not all of the food processors I fix might be broken."

Athena fought to smile beatifically. "I was talking about the other drawbacks."

Artemis' brow furrowed in thought. "Um . . . you start running out of shelves?"

To the casual eye, Athena's immaculate smile might have looked slightly strained.

"No, sister dear. Sooner or later, you'll be expected to read magazines like *Motoring Monthly* simply because of your gender."

"So? Driving's easy. That is," she added, "as long as you remember that when you want the horseless chariot to go left, you push the round bit that way . . . or is it that way . . .?"

The observant eye might have noticed that froth was appearing at the corners of Athena's mouth and a slight grinding motion could be perceived in the vicinity of her teeth.

"Artemis, how would you like to spend the rest of your life living up to a stereotyped image of women just as men have had to do for the last forty centuries?"

Artemis considered it. "What, like Aphrodite?"

Athena gave a smile that could have shattered glass. "Yes, like Aphrodite."

Artemis put on a deeply cunning expression. "Ah, but I don't know any men like Aphrodite."

Put it like this, Artemis. The Voice smoothly interrupted Athena's howl. *Ares is the God of War but as a person, he's a wimp.*

Ares woke up and glowered.

However, being male he must feign machismo. If women rule the world, you'll have to act domineering, in control—

"I can do that!" Artemis put on a stern bawl. "You, lackey! Fetch me your master! I demand a refund, Mr Safeway! Ho there, landlord! A pint—"

—and intelligent.

"—of your finest bee— Oh." Artemis deflated.

"What's your *point*, Athena?" Apollo pleaded tiredly. "We've been listening to you rant on for aeons now."

Athena stroked Pooky thoughtfully. "You want me to condense the essence of humanity's oldest prejudice? Do you not see that it will be unfair if any one sex rules the world – not only for the oppressed gender but for the dominant gender, as individuals will have to fulfil a stereotyped generalisation regardless of the fact that they are free and unique beings?"

Aphrodite started going cross-eyed. It's tough when your IQ is only marginally larger than your shoesize.

"However, if you, as players in the Divine game, agree to put your Cards on top of the Joker before the Holy Computer re-commences Game-Time, we can start afresh without having to destroy the world and give the humans a chance to remove inequality between the sexes."

"What's in it for us?" Hermes asked.

"Nothing." Athena's eyes became glittering obsidian chips and everyone was sharply reminded why she was the Goddess of Wisdom. "But I resent becoming non-existent. If I go, I'll drag the rest of this megalomaniac family down with me."

Says who?

There was an ominous silence. The clashing of the two wills was almost palpable. The outcome was inevitable – the Voice was the ruler of the gods, but Athena had more practise at staring people down.

Fundamentally, perhaps, the Voice didn't have anything to glare *with*.

You have Our Divine Word of Honour that We will not oppose you. There, They added sulkily. *We hope you're satisfied.*

"Not yet. I need the gods to swear too."

"You want us to swear?" Apollo sat up cheerfully. "Those of a nervous disposition please leave the room. Someone pass me the Hungarian Dictionary in case I need inspiration—"

An icicle-loaded glare from Athena silenced him.

Zeus put one hand on his heart and solemnly led the gods and goddesses in their ceremonious vow, a rite as old as time itself.

"I vow to hand over all my Cards. Hop three times. Cross me heart and hope to die, stick a needle in me eye."

"Great!" Athena declared in tones of mild hysteria. "Slow-motion video, lacy italics, can we please hurry up? The Holy Computer's going to re-connect itself soon!"

On-cue, the Holy Computer flickered.

20480 KB OK? PREPARE FOR SYSTEM RE-START . . .

229

En masse, the residents of Olympus lurched to the Card table, brandishing their Cards.

"Is that everyone?" Athena croaked anxiously.

"No. I've just got to . . ." Hermes fumbled with his robes. "Where did I . . . Got them!" He waved a handful of purloined Cards. "I took them off Hades when . . . whoops . . ."

. . . 10 . . .

With inexorable inevitability, the three of hearts slowly peeled away and fluttered to the floor.

. . . 9 . . .

Hermes swooped to the floor, lunging after it.

. . . 8 . . .

The rest of the Cards liberated themselves with scratchy flaps and fanned out across the Hall.

. . . 7 . . .

Poseidon plucked a Card from his trident.

. . . 6 . . .

Apollo dived to the floor and desperately snatched up a scattered Card.

. . . 5 . . .

Athena grabbed the rest of the Cards and began to count hastily.

. . . 4 . . .

"There's one missing!" she yowled in anguish, as Aphrodite stirred and eyed the Card drifting towards her.

. . . 3 . . .

She blinked languidly, indifferent.

. . . 2 . . .

The Voice exerted Their Will, sending the delinquent Card winging upwards.

. . . 1 . . .

Athena snatched the Card frantically out of the air and rammed the fistful onto the table.

. . . 0 . . .

Time and reality stood poised on the fulcrum of possibility.

Then . . .

RE-ASSESSMENT OF GLOBAL REIGN; A STATE OF NEAR-BALANCE HAS BEEN ACHIEVED BETWEEN THE TWO DOMINANT SPECIES, MAN AND WOMAN. PREPARE TO BEGIN GAME.

Athena sagged with relief. An excited babble rose from the denizens of Olympus and a festive mood invaded the Hall. Better still – the sandwich boy had just arrived and today he had Marmite.

Athena, boomed the Voice, in what They probably thought was a conspiratorial whisper, *how long before people start noticing the changes?*

"A couple of decades," she said eventually. "Humans – or huwomans? – have to think they're making all the changes themselves."

The Voice mulled over this. *Athena, you just got that video of the Other Places from a comedy show. You didn't really know what would happen if you played both the Jokers, did you?*

Athena thought about it. "No," she finally conceded. "How did You work it out?"

The Voice grinned. Metaphorically speaking. *You're not the only person who watches "Morecambe and Wise."*

Robert Passfield (15)

Edward Goodacre (8)

*Medusa

Long hair, midnight black
Brushes her face
Like a veil.

Long, fish-like hair
With snapping, forked tongues.

Her delicate hands
Plucking flowers in her garden.

Stony hands, hard as boulders.

Her young body
As smooth as a butterfly wing.

Her skinny stomach
With ribs showing,
Squeezing against her scaly skin.

As a child, skipping merrily
Through the wood
In and out of trees.

Now her legs,
Crusty as lizards,
Gouge out the ground.

Hannah Edwards (8)

Castle by a River
(Karl Friedrich Schinkel 1820)

I know you asked me
For an architectural drawing,
But I'm sorry, I just couldn't help it –
So, forgive me
For the peacocks with their beautiful turquoise tails,
For the deer with his velvet horns,
For the dove with her ivory wings,
For the red, silky roses,
For the tree with its shimmering leaves.

Paniz Shahkarami (13)

*Women of War

Women of the meadows!
Women, waiting!
Women of tight hope
     Walking along the never-ending desert,
     The desert of hope,
     Aware of every reverberating sound.

Women of mud-dressed streams!
Women of flames of a thousand pillars, smoking to the
  high sky!
Women of faraway loves!
     Days of silence and work,
      Nights of strain.

Daytime women,
   Running
     Without fatigue,
      And at night,
       Degradation.

Despair.
Eyes and looks
Darken the fragrance of the words of the poet.

Women come and go in the foggy meadow;
Shamed women!
   Stumbling through the dew
     Falling from the fog.

From the wound of the heart,
From the breasts of which of you was blood dripping?

Nights dimmed with drizzling rain –
When there is no food, no work, no hope –
Which one of you will lie awake? –
In the bed of despondent harshness,
In the bed of tight-hearted tension,[1]
In the bed of painful thoughts of your secrets and
  passions;
Remembering the agony and pain –
To light,
Till late, the flame of fire
In your open eyes.

Which of you will now lustre,
    The armaments of the Abai[2]
        For the day of revenge?

1 *Tight-hearted tension* comes from a Persian phrase used when
someone misses another person.
2 The Abai is a fictional Turkish hero.

IN THE DISTANT FIRMAMENT

Lizzie Bone (14)

Ben Womack (12)

*The Way into Manhood

"*Useless,*" screamed Mr Lett. "*Utterly useless.*"

Paul stayed silent at the shout. He leant his young, fair head to stare at the grey carpet and his Dennis the Menace slippers.

Sam watched his father yell what he always yelled at his younger brother, about how his brain was so full of rubbish he would never learn, about how he ought to work rather than play. Children, according to Mr Lett, were meant to act and work like adults. Adults weren't big children; children were small adults.

Sam sighed. His father's home-spun philosophies, he knew, came from a home where he was slapped with a belt every night, for a reason that was good enough not to tell Sam. His father never mentioned his mother. She had died at an early age.

The shouting continued.

Sam's mother, washing the old greasy pans that were from someone they didn't know as a late wedding present, sighed. She dreaded the day when her small boy would get it in his head to talk back. Then their heads really would ring.

The telephone rang.

Sam ran to get it.

"Hello?"

A long buzz echoed down the line.

Sam walked back into the kitchen.

"Who was it?" said his mother over the swish of the water.

"A wrong number."

"Oh."

Both were tired of Mr Lett. His mother continued washing. The shouting continued.

The phone rang again.

"I'd leave it."

"OK."

The phone carried on ringing. In the cauldron of Sam's head, the sounds swirled up into a spell of claustrophobia. His head ached, drooping off his shoulders and hitting on the floor like a lump of hot, wet fat.

An eruption from the volcanoes in the front room.

"Will one of you two answer the phone?"

It was Sam. He stood up, scraping the chair back on the floor. He picked up the phone.

"Hello?"

A buzz, going through his head like water, swirling down a broken drain.

The shouting continued.

It was enough.

"Why don't you ever leave him alone, Dad? Why can't you accept that he's a child?"

"Why, why, why. Can't you think of anything else but why?" his father spat. His father sat in a chair, by the empty fireplace, curled up, like some dead bat.

"I know he's a child. My child. And I want to teach him a bit of the world, in case he grows up bad."

"The only part of the world that you can teach him is misery."

"Well that's what I didn't teach you enough of. And look at what happened."

"What did happen?"

"You're growing up, lad. Think about it yourself."

A crumpled paper dart, thrown into a dustbin. Sam ran away, to the haven of upstairs. With his elder brother struck down, defeated, Paul's walls were breached and

239

soon the patch of light grey carpet by his feet became dark grey from his tears.

Mrs Lett would have come in. But she was already half deaf from the last time.

The children slept. Or rather, the child and the "young man".

Paul slept immediately, rolled into the infant position under his sheets. But Sam was kept awake. Not by the shouting downstairs – no, he was used to that – but because his father's words had hurt him. He was twelve. His birthday had been three weeks ago, and already, to Mr Lett, he was an old man. I suppose he was only thinking of the business, thought Sam. A swear word down below stopped his thoughts. That meant that it was bad.

Uncomfortably, Sam shut his eyes.

Sam slept.

am slept.

m slet.

slt.

s.

It was a good day. Blue skies and all that stuff. He was riding a bicycle. It didn't have a basket, but he felt a weight on his back – a rucksack. The bike was a present. Great bike. Its name? Down there on the bar.

SPIDERMAN

Sam skidded through Portakabins. Slung his weight backwards to go on one wheel. There were a lot of Portakabins, with kids cross-sectioning through the pathways between them. Sam felt safe. His hair flew back from his forehead. He stood up on the pedals, as if angels' wings had suddenly appeared on his back. It felt good. It felt so good, wishing he was a bird. Maybe he'd grow to be a bird. Or a super hero. His chubby fingers pulled, skidding to a halt. In front of him was a large, rigid white sign. The tight, black letters sprung out.

~~PLEASE~~ GET OFF YOUR BICYCLE

Sam got off. Strange notice, he thought, as he wheeled the bike. Not very polite, but perhaps vandals had spray-painted the line across the "please". But it looked too precise, too like a teacher's writing, to be vandals. Teachers, hell, what did they know. All they wanted you to do was take exams. Oh, of course they have their reasons. To protect you from vandals and stuff. But, for some reason, he didn't think that the place he was in would have any vandals. Couldn't see any girls either, worst luck. He walked on. He was wearing trainers. They pinched his feet. His hands felt cramped holding the bike. The wheel at the front of the bike gave a loud groan, then stopped. Kicking it for safety, he carried on. Sam left the Portakabins, and was now walking, with the others. There were others, all amazed. They were in a city. A city which had small, squat buildings. Almost bungalows.

His front wheel hit the next sign. A bright white sign.

NO RUCKSACKS

Sam slung it off his shoulder. He laid it by his feet and then walked on. Perhaps there was something in it. Who cares. The creak started to disturb him, continuing as he pushed it along. He'd stop the problem, like a doctor. He knelt down, by the oily mass. Maybe he wanted to be a doctor. He touched the pedal. Something fell on to his hand. It left sticky paste on it, which he rubbed off on the grass. It was the letter D. He looked at the word. Letters were dropping off.

PI E MAN

He looked around. There was an eternity of bending people, so he was still not alone. But he could not see them as they, he was sure, could not see him. He thought about their bicycles, all different colours, all different makes, each with its own pattern. All bicycles though. All created. Just like the world. He walked on, dreamily, leaving the black letter D on the grass, looking like some contorted worm. The city was behind Sam now. In front of him, a forest loomed, the dark green trees contrasting violently with the bright blue sky. The bright blue sky. Sam remembered how once, he had been to a place with a sky like that. Then the sky had turned golden. A sunset. He smiled. That was the untouchable, simple beauty of nature. You shouldn't take photographs of it, trap it still in a lifeless hollow box. Let it blow with the winds. He looked around, and saw them. Some people were running, pushing their bikes and talking to others. Sound washed around Sam's brain, a loud, booming carnival. He waited. No one came up to him. So he laughed to himself. He'd blend in later. He walked towards the forest.

NO LAUGHTER

Hammered to a tree, with squat nails. Somehow, this sign robbed all the goodness out of this place. Sam stopped in the sudden, violent hush that struck down on him and the only sound heard was the SQUEAK, SQUEAK, SQUEAK of a wheel, that could've been his, or it could've been blowing in the wind. It was his though, he thought. So did everyone else.

There was silence. It felt as if it was someone else's silence, a loan that would shortly have to be paid back. Then, words started. Mumblings about subjects of no importance. He sighed and walked on. He couldn't stand that boring place.

So into the woods. A dark canopy above, roots that tripped you up beneath. The moans echoed through the woods, moans of all the wheels as they spun round in their 360 degree existence. There was a crunch as Sam trod on a piece of paint that had fallen off. The orange underneath was a blaze of rusted glory. It looked almost touchable, but he didn't want to touch it. Some air must've got through the protective coating of zinc. Zinc, being above in the series from iron, absorbed all the air. If it was broken, then Iron Oxide was formed (FeO), being rust. You never knew when little snippets of information could come in handy in later life. Getting a job, etc, etc. The words his old teacher had spoken to him stuck in his mind, and he wished that, when at school, he had paid more attention.

The woods were a dark place. Barely any light shone through those high boughs. In the black, Sam's thoughts drifted and so did his feet. The little light stopped, leaving Sam alone in a very dark place. Except for the sounds. The bicycles were deafening, like a colony of bats shrieking. Sam had never understood why they did that. One day, he might learn.

Sam still walked into it. Couldn't see a darned thing.

The sign must have been weak, because it broke and swooped to the floor. Beetles scuttled away, their temporary habitat destroyed. Sam shut his eyes as a foggy dust blew into his eyes from underneath the sign. A few leaves blew, but he couldn't see them, as they fluttered about his ankles.

LEAVE YOUR BIKES HERE

Most of it was guesswork, but he was a good guesser. Besides, his eyes were becoming accustomed to the dark.

Either that, or it was getting lighter. Either way, he could see. Then, in front of him, through a doorway in the trees, a huge pile of dead bicycles lay, cold and grey, reminding him of the terrible photos from Auschwitz, of countless piles of briefcases belonging to the dead. No atrocity was visible here. But there was a feel that there was something, something bad. An ethereal fire seemed to glow from within them, lighting them with a pale blue shade. He tripped over his bicycle as he let it go, his hands as numb as the metal. PIE was gone, leaving just:

MAN

A metal avalanche drowned other broken bikes as Sam, mud caking his face so the only sign of skin was where his tears fled down his face, hurled the broken old toy at the pile. There was a silence, broken only by a few clanks as the bikes moved. Sam looked around. Time clearly had done its work. Yet, written in thick, peeling black letters, every bike read Man. The truth burnt him.

There was a fire, it was everywhere. What else to do but run?

He left that metal place, his legs straining under him. He was running as fast as he could and to him that seemed painfully slow. He was running on a beach. The tide broke and shot bullets of water at his face.

It was a fitness exercise. There were others. There would always be others.

A stone in the sand. A shoelace, fixed like a tripwire. Whatever it was, it happened.

He fell.

He looked up. Tall above him were grey office blocks, towering up into clouds of broken dream dust. There was a fog. He walked to the door. A button. Above it his name, carved in intricate, gold plating. Everyone was watching him, but there was no one there. There would be a row of buttons, a row of buttons for everyone. Why couldn't he be different?

He turned.

Around him, like brown splashes of paint a clumsy artist had destroyed his masterpiece with, sat the men. And the women. And the children. But, of course, they weren't like him. They couldn't reach the red button.

He went into a room. In it was another sign, bricked in into the silver wall.

PUT ON THE ASSIGNED SUIT

He put it on. It was too big for him. The sleeves stretched out over his hands. Out of a panel in the wall came a suitcase. He held it. It was probably leather. In front of him, a door opened, a door that flooded the room with glorious light.

He was in the desert. It was hot. No tree bleached the landscape. Another sign, on the wire fence behind him. All around him, stretching out far.

THIS IS YOUR FUTURE
ENJOY IT

There he was, a boy in a suit in a desert.

He never woke up.

Kirsten Donaldson (17)

Mahlete-Tsigé Getachew (16)

*Sentient Darkness

Is that you? Mother?

It is night.
  It was night then too.
  I lie in the sentient darkness and wonder what we have become.

We have come a long way, but we have come in the wrong direction.

"Peter, are you ready to hit the Outside?"

We always had been a trio. As children we were the Unholy Trinity, children being the subjective word. We never had a real childhood, the norm in this bizarre age. Oh, I know about youth, strangely enough. I read those smuggled books, Enid Blyton and her ilk. Children, the twentieth century would like us to believe, are carefree innocent beings. Quaint thought.

As delinquents, we were Noble Peter Fox, after my cousin's friend. He's dead now. Both of them.

Noble, we realised straight away, had to be Noble. We didn't know and couldn't imagine anyone more thoughtful, more generous and more downright noble than Noble.

Fox was Fox, unbelievably cool and remarkably sharp. Fox has two facial expressions which can mean anything; a lean smile and a ferocious grin. Both are so overtly dishonest that punters assume they are failed attempts at intelligence and Street know-how; Fox, they cunningly cogitate, is an imbecile. They usually discover the truth much later.

Which left me to be Peter, which is silly, really, as I'm female. We all are. All right, so it's hard to tell, what with my skinhead hairdo and the fact that I look like a direct descendant of the stick insect, but I like to think I have feminine eyes.

"Ready, Noble."
   "Fox?"
   "Uh-huh." She licked dry lips, her fierce, Atlantic-grey eyes darting warily around.
   "To the Outside, ladies."

"The Outside." We echoed the toast, exchanged nervous smiles. We were committed. We put on our VirtuHeadsets and lay back on our bunks.

Incidentally, the skinhead haircut isn't a matter of choice. My hair fell out in my fleeting infancy and hasn't grown back since. I decided against purchasing a wig from one of the fences partly because I would never have enough credits to afford one but mostly because I thought I'd survive longer on the Street if I looked like a homicidal maniac. I've been right – so far.

We were in.

The vast expanse of the Realm swept away from us, a crystal chessboard beneath a ravenous dome that reached into infinity and beyond.

This was a dimension of unnatural regularity and perfect symmetry; the world was flat and the tracks of possibility stretched away like a textbook illustration of vanishing perspective. This was Virtual Reality.

Twenty-first century scientists were right when they said that the only restrictions to what we could create in virtual reality were those enforced by an "unnecessary" sense of ethics. Twenty-second century scientists were the Smart Alecs who thought of handing virtual reality over to amoral robots.

Previously, virtual reality was only used as a mock-battlefield for military forces. Then, some Class D droid came up with the wonderful idea of tailor-made heaven for the wealthy and mighty. Electrodes attached to a person's brain could read their ultimate dreams and desires and make them materialise in VirtuHeaven.

It took a human to think of creating tailored hells. At first, they were hailed as a humane alternative to the death sentence, the standard punishment being about a week in VirtuHell. A week in VirtuHell is plenty of time.

Criminals prepared to sell their daughters to greasy interplanetary traders for a unit of electro-opium tended to emerge from VirtuHell weeping for their mothers or begging to be accepted by a holy order. Some would say nothing upon release but were found days later hanging from a serpent-like noose, their incomprehensible suicide notes a frighteningly desperate scribble.

Then, the punishments started getting longer. And VirtuHell started being used in torture. And the Families, instead of getting contracts on people, would order them to be captured – and put into VirtuHell.

Overnight, the entire atmosphere of the Street changed. There was a tension, an edge as palpable as the serrated blade of a knife pushed against your throat. The smuggled literature I used to read always talked about the smell of the sea being a tangible thing. It was like that. The Street lost its greasy, intimate scent. The air was filled with "D"s – despair, darkness, desperation, death.

Save for the eerie blue glow of the possibility tracks there was no light, making it hard to scan the horizon for trouble. In the distant firmament, myriads of remote "stars" glittered. They were interfaces between the Realm and reality. I craned my head, seeking our interface.

People have been known to lose their interface and be stranded in the Realm, wandering aimlessly about, telling of dragons and mermaids and the time they were Head of the Families. A few are rescued. Most never find their way home, and their families unwittingly keep the body preserved, condemning the ghosts to an eternity of the Realm.

There was our lonely star, forming the tip of the Dragon Constellation's tail. Reassured, I turned and followed the plunging Noble and Fox.

Everyone has a vice on the Street. Everything you do is to fund your habit. Your habit is someone else's business. Their business funds their particular vice. All our money, our meagre dishonest incomes, flow to one of the great Families that exercise steely control. We're not even marionettes in the hands of the Families; no, that's the government.

My vice; books. You may have gathered that by now. Scruffy little paperbacks with words printed on paper that you have to read. Nothing as sophisticated as a brainchip, although I have been known to settle for a knowledge transplant when the text was particularly contraband.

Fox's vice? Various narcotic concoctions known by the all-encompassing term "Stuff". If she wants to blast out her brain with powdered plants, that's fine by me, as long as she leaves me alone to fill my head with fantastical tales from a bygone age.

Fox always swears that she only uses soft Stuff but I'm not so sure. Lately, she has been rather wild-eyed. Her crafty smile is losing its edge and she is starting to sound almost neurotic.

Then again, we all are.

And Noble's vice? Hacking, I believe the twentieth-century verb is.

She tried describing it to me, once. The rush of adrenaline, the thrill of knowing that you were defying the Families and one day you would be caught – one day but not today. Absolute anonymity allowing you to create your own persona. She – *Noble*! – could execute countless brilliant manoeuvres and no one would be any closer to knowing who she was.

"It's like being God," she said lunging closer, her face flushed.

"Or an author," I agreed fervently.

She leaned back, baffled.

"Pre-twenty-second-century writer of fiction texts stored in brainchips," I translated.

"I suppose," she said politely.

"Assume disguises," Noble said tersely.

Noble is always earnest in the actual world and strangely grim in the Virtuals. The transition is terrifyingly smooth and utter. Being in a Virtual tends to bring out the latent aspects of your personality and the truth can be unpleasant.

It was inevitable, really. Everyone on the Street lives in hope of making it to the glorious Outside, yet we all live in terror of the Families who control the Gates to the Outside.

We were about seventeen, which is old for Street-dwellers. I say "about" because we had no way of knowing for sure. We looked seventeen but felt seventy.

Noble came home one night, her eyes wild, her face feverish. Somehow, we knew what she was going to say even before she said it.

"We're going to escape to the Outside."

Our silence demanded an explanation.

"We access the main System through a Virtual, just as we always do in routine jobs. This time, however, we'll disguise ourselves as mundane repair programs so we can travel through all levels of the Realm until we reach the Portals. Once we've passed the Portals, we'll shed our disguises and race to the Gates where we leave photoscan permits of ourselves with the droids there. We exit the Virtual and return to reality. We hitch a ride to the Gate. The droids will have photoscan permits of us and droids don't ask questions. We'll be in – or rather, we'll be Out – in under three hours."

"It'll cost an awful lot of credits to hire a decent Virtual interface and convincing disguise programs."

"Once we're Outside, we won't need credits. They use these metal coins and paper notes."

"If we're caught—"

"We won't *be* caught! No one will stop a trio of *repair* programs."

"I don't know if I'm prepared to sacrifice my Stuff credits for some madcap scheme of yours, Noble."

"You'll be able to get all the Stuff you'll ever want Outside, Fox."

"But what if I can't wait that long, what if . . ." Fox sought to articulate the insecurity only an addict can ever feel.

"Four weeks without any precious fixes, that's all I'm asking! Just think, all the credits you spend – ten a week is it? – could go towards buying perfect disguises, state-of-the-art Virtuals and we could be free, for ever! Surely that's worth anything?"

A year earlier, we'd have said no. A year earlier, we'd have been capable of laughter and would have laughed at the idea; we'd have been less jaded by Street existence, less desperate.

We drifted downwards, slipping into the grey latex suits that had cost us everything. They were so sophisticated they even had droid voice-simulators that would convert our words into the mechanical drone of a repair program.

"Fox, you're an angel!" Noble exclaimed when she first saw them. "What contacts do you have that you're not telling us about?"

Fox blinked rapidly. "Noble, this scheme of yours had better work."

"With these outfits?" Noble purred. "Of course it will."

As we approached the possibility tracks, we could see programs whizzing frantically through them, being greedily slurped up like bubbles in a straw. The tracks vibrated faintly, the busier ones humming with a note as pure and poignant as an angel's heart breaking.

We dived in to be bathed in radiant blue.

"Noble, I think—"

We were swept aside by a bulky subpoena muttering "Confidential; confidential."

We got to our feet and dusted off our disguises. "We need to—"

This time, it was a spry request for an overdraft that knocked us over as it darted past squealing "Emergency; emergency."

"Keep moving," Noble's neutral voice instructed us.

We staggered to our droid feet and lurched into movement. "Repair," we murmured soothingly. "Repair; repair."

Outside, I promised myself, I'm going to buy a book a month. A book a week.

We skated through the possibility track unchallenged. Countless programs swept past, a wealth of information flowing betwixt us. We could have made our fortunes there and then simply by hijacking a credit transfer file. But we wouldn't have been free.

There are seven Levels between the Realm and the Portals. We had never gone beyond Level Four.

I may even buy myself a wig. I toyed with the notion.

Tension so solid you have to carve your way through; fear so real it almost speaks.

Blonde? Brunette?

With each Level, the intensity is heightened fractionally. Programs rush past more frenetically, the buzzing gets louder and higher-pitched, the vibrating becomes mad rocking, the pace is accelerated, the screw is twisted tighter. By the time you reach Level Two, you think you've gone mad.

Or maybe I'll just stay bald, as an appropriate reminder of the Street.

Level One.

The gentle blue light was now a harsh white glare. Unexpected corners and crosses loomed up in the skidding possibility tracks. We didn't dare crash for fear of the droids; we didn't dare slow down for fear of the droids. The temptation to panic was hard to resist.

"Repair;" I gasped tensely. "Repair; repair; re—"

Suddenly, the Portals reared up like sea-serpents, massive and vaguely threatening. We surged to a halt and stood in the mock-celestial radiance, the lurid glow sending sharp shadows reeling.

"Welcome to the Portals," stated a melodious voice in precise, diamond-clear tones. Too high to be male, too low to be female, too warm to be droid, too clinical to be human.

"You will state your rank." It sounded faintly amused. Obviously a private joke.

"Repair program 14AX68B-T." We spoke in ragged unison.

We stood poised, waiting for the clamp of steel droid pincers on our arms. Einstein was right – time is curved; several eternities passed in the space of a second. The nearer your death approaches, the slower the moments pass.

"Access granted." It was an angel, deigning to impart wisdom to asinine mortals. I wanted to fall to my knees and shed tears over the Portals, thanking the aloof voice for its goodness. Instead, I merely nodded curtly, as a repair program would.

The Portals swung open revealing a vast expanse, the route to the great Outside.

We crept through.

Space. An agoraphobe's nightmare. The Outside beckoned to us, it summoned us home.

"We did it!" Noble squealed, starlight – synthetic starlight – wandering down her ebony face. "This time tomorrow, we'll be out of here, enjoying the high life! We're free, Peter, we—"

"Let's make it to the Gates first, Noble." Despite my stern words, I was every bit as delighted as Noble.

"FREE!!" Austere Noble performed a double-flip.

I was aware of Fox's listless presence behind me. "Don't worry, Fox," I said warmly. "The ordeal is almost over."

"It wouldn't have worked."

"Fox?"

"It wouldn't have worked anyway."

Noble slewed around in a desperate arc. "What does she mean, *anyway*? It's working, isn't it?"

Fox was already shaking her head. "You see, you see . . ."

Noble shot forwards, her hands clutching at Fox's latex suit.

"Leave her, Noble, she doesn't know what she's saying. We've been stationary for too long!"

Noble ignored me and shook Fox. "Anyway? Why did you say that?"

Fox's head drooped forwards, her hair hanging in twisted locks.

"Fox, tell me!" She shook her again and Fox's head rolled back. Her bare neck was unnaturally bent and gleamed strangely in the alien moonlight. From the workings of her exposed throat, I could tell that Fox was laughing.

"Noble, we have to—"

"Fools, fools," Fox murmured drowsily.

"Noble!" I grabbed her arm and hauled her around. Fox slipped gracelessly to the ground. "She's obviously on a trip of some kind. It is imperative that we keep moving. Once we've reached the Gates—"

"You won't reach the Gates. The Families are expecting you."

I felt the world plummeting away from me, leaving me in the hungry black void. I crouched by Fox.

"They're expecting us? Why?"

"Because I told them we'd be coming. That's why they gave us such good disguises."

So much sadness.

Diamonds danced in her eyelashes. "I couldn't wait that long. And what if it failed? I'd have gone mad without my Stuff."

"And so you chose to tell the Families." Until then, I had never thought Noble capable of bitterness.

"Choice wasn't involved, it was a matter of necessity!"

"How much did they promise you, Fox? Thirty pieces of silver?" My mouth was full of ashes. I found I was crying; crying because there are no true friends and innocence died when man was born; because when Pandora opened that box, she released hope – the greatest evil of them all; because I, like a babe, yearned after my mother.

Fox's head snapped back and her eyes narrowed. "Three hundred," she snarled, her voice steeped in the iceberg-grey of her eyes. "To be paid as soon as you've been delivered to the Families."

Oh Fox, naive, foolish Fox.

Noble's gentle brown eyes widened in disbelief.

"They didn't pay you?" I croaked.

"They promised—" she began defiantly.

I closed my eyes and shook my head. "Promised. Do you imagine that the promise of the Families is worth any more than a pauper's spit?" I was incandescent in my grief, towering in my rage. The stars were falling from their heavens. "How much of your blood money do you think you'll receive? One credit? Two? Or do you think, now that they've got all three of us in this trap of theirs, they'll let you go?"

She backed away, gazelle-like in her fear. She was no longer Fox, she was Fawn. And the silver-grey wolves were closing around us. "They swore they wouldn't hurt you—"

CAUGHT!

Steel cages slammed down. A mass of sentry-droids swarmed around. They wrestled with electrodes that squirmed and spat their electric-blue venom.

Welcome to VirtuHell, a droid creakily informed me as it pushed an electrode towards my resisting head.

Who says sarcasm is a lost art?

I felt the familiar ripple as actual became virtual and reality changed . . .

And didn't change.

I didn't move. It is useless to attempt escape in VirtuHell. There is no-where, no-when to flee to. You cannot even contemplate thought. I was in the hands of the Families. Hands have no compassion.

I realised this was a cunning ploy of theirs; let me assume I was safe, let me relax, then—!

What was my personal hell?

. . . those sleepless nights at the orphanage waiting for a grey dawn that, here, would never come . . .

. . . unarmed on the Street . . .

. . . an eternity of this tension, would that drive me mad in the end? . . .

. . . boredom so absolute and endless I would be screaming for mercy, desperate for release of any sort . . .

I sniffed the air. (You can do that, in the more sophisticated Virtuals, such as the one we had unwisely penetrated. Unfortunately, this also means that the experience is less virtual and more absolute. Plenty pain, zero gain.)

It had the familiar tang of ozone. I was in VirtuHell, no doubt about that. In that case, why was it no different to reality?

257

Comprehension crashed over me like a vengeful tidal wave.

They didn't need to design a VirtuHell for me. I already lived in one – my reality.

Welcome to yesterday's twenty-third century, where the only glimmer of light in my grim and prospectless future is the knowledge that I have two friends.

Welcome to tomorrow's twenty-third century where I have a choice between being stranded in VirtuHell until my body dies or returning to the actual world and living in constant dread of the faceless killer who the Families will one day send for me, unable to trust even Noble since I have already been betrayed.

Ladies and gentlemen, the choice is yours. What will it be?

Noble chose not to return to the actual world. For all I know, she could still be writhing in agony in a VirtuHell somewhere. I left her body where it was.

Fox . . . Fox isn't well. Her skin is stretched impossibly taut over her skull and her eyes seem to have lost the necessity to blink and the ability to focus. She is observing something humans were never intended to see.

Is she happy? She laughs. Constantly. But laughter is not the same as happiness, and the insane, desperate sound Fox makes when spoken to is only a very distant relative of laughter. I don't think she knows who I am. I don't think she knows who she is.

I cannot tell the authorities. They are weak, dithering fools controlled by the putrid stink of credits. They are the slaves of the Families.

What, then, am I to do? Am I to humbly wait for the assassin's knife? Am I to hope the Families will forgive me and yet live in perpetual terror of retribution? Am I to continue to behave as if nothing has happened, and I am unchanged?

I have purchased some Safricide-D. Innocuous stuff when diluted. Lethal when not.

What now?

What do you do when the worst possible nightmare the technology of the twenty-third century can create for you is no different to your life?

It is hardly an inspiring thought. I know.

If real hell exists the Christians could be right – an eternity of pits of fire – or the Greeks – pushing rocks up mountains and so forth.

It doesn't matter who's right. Nothing is worse than living with this knowledge, the impossible burden of knowing that there is no longer any time for hope and no longer any hope for time.

I have prepared myself for every eventuality. I am ready.

And so I lie in the sentient darkness, marvelling at how far and how quickly we have tumbled.

We don't need god, we don't need a devil.

We have each other.

We have ourselves.

They will lie to you. They will tell you that darkness is simply a state of light.

Don't believe them. Darkness is omniscient, it knows exactly what it is doing.

It is here now, around me. It is whispering sweet promises. I am resisting it. I will not yield.

Oh, it is clever. It has assured me that it can lead me to my unknown parents. Hush, can you hear it?

I will not heed its beguiling voice. It is deceptive and we will fall further.

I yearn to push through this impersonal page and re-write myself into an Enid Blyton book.

"I say, Ralph!" pleaded Peter, grey eyes dancing. "We must stop advocating amoral applications of science and start worrying about the growing crime culture within our peer group. What ripping fun!"

Mmmm . . . perhaps not.

They will lie to you.

I wonder if I am capable of thought any longer. Even this darkness is more self-aware than I am. My limbs are there. I cannot feel them, but I know they are there.

Much that I thought I knew has now turned out to be false. Maybe I'm wrong, and my limbs aren't there.

Maybe I have never existed; maybe I have always existed.

Only the darkness is eternal.

Mother?

Jessie Errey (15)

*The Last Supper

She closes the front door behind her and walks to the corner of Marlowe Avenue, looking around for a sign of someone, just in case.

Of course there is nobody to watch her. It's just a fading tradition from Before. There was a body in the house but it didn't smell very bad. It was too far gone for that, just bones and high-heeled shoes. She took the high heels; she needs some nice shoes for when she and her husband eat a good dinner together and they'll go very well with her new suit. The silence crushes all around her, and her blue linen skirt suit is bright in the grey street as she runs, clickety-clack in the shoes, back to the warehouse.

She is coming. I can hear her sharp shoes ringing on the pavement. The vibrations created by her clanging feet disturb a puddle nearby and the layer of scum, like the topping of a pie, reverberates gently with each step. The sound is too loud and the heels too spindly. She must have been in one of the houses for those new shoes. I hope she didn't see any more corpses. They often frighten her, helpless and empty-eyed, and other times she wants to bury them. I am too tired to dig any more holes.

The water that flows from the pipes in the sluice is slowly dwindling. A week ago when it was warm, there was little more than a muddy trickle. One of the old factory windows has smashed in last night's storm. Tonight we will sleep in the warehouse.

I am sitting on a pile of bricks, radiant with warmth from the day's humidity. It will rain tonight. The sky is black above the unkempt white houses. Roses glow in the

261

Joanna Halyburton (16)

straggly gardens, saturated in golden-dark light; roses that nobody has touched in a long time. Sometimes I bring her back a rose; she likes white ones, but when I find them they have usually shrivelled and gone brown. There are red roses, though, red and pink roses that clash burning in the rusty glow. The paving stones are scabby and leprous from years of disuse. The leaves are prematurely decayed on the trees. The world is sick and gnarled: we no longer have domestic needs or modern duties. Our property is infinite; summer is only just beginning to die; I miss the constraints of certain survival.

She has sneaked up on me. She must have taken the shoes off; I did not hear her come. She pushes aside the hair at the nape of my neck and kisses me, licks at a callous of grime in my ear. She is all dressed up and has put in the shoulder pads that I found her in the big department store. Her skirt is dusty but it smells clean and the linen is still fresh and bright. She must have got stockings from somewhere. Bristles are poking through the sheer nylon, but she will always have great legs. I suck her finger like a puppy and fondle the bead on her necklace. I made her this necklace, out of a shell and a string and a bead, Before, when it was fashionable to live frugally. We are no longer denied objects that we want. There is nobody to charge us. We browse through the ruins of the department store for new clothes. I have a woollen suit that I used to keep clean for birthdays and Christmas hanging on a hook in the warehouse. I look good in suits. She is made up; I recognize her perfume as Chanel No. 5. She is still a very good-looking woman; she has good taste and good legs. I kiss her on the lips, and then again on the crown of her long nose.

"I brought you something," she says, and hands me a bone. I think it's a good one. It's not dry yet, and although the meat is bad, there's plenty of marrow inside.

"Where did you get this from?" I ask her. She smiles; she isn't going to tell me. She wants me to ask, but a wife's secrets are always kept.

I tell her I will cut some marrow out and make a soup for tonight; I tell her to start collecting water. She has a scab on her lip. I think it's from the bad water. Soon she'll be fine, she just needs time to rest, is all. "No," she tells me. "I want you to get into your linen suit, and I want us to have a nice dinner. We're going to have a feast. I picked something up along the way."

She's going to show me some fruit she's found. There's not much of it around, not much that hasn't been eaten by worms or didn't drop off the trees when everybody started getting sick. She drags something out, but it isn't fruit. It's a cat. Blood is streaming from a hole in its skull. Her face is glowing. "I killed it myself with a stone. It's still warm. The blood's warm. Feel it." She dips her finger into its head and paints a moustache on me. I look at the cat. Blood is clogging its eyes. To impress her, I put my mouth to the cat's head, and suck. It's good, warm blood. She laughs as I knew she would.

"You're clever, darling," I say. "I didn't know there were any animals left alive. You're sure it's not sick?"

"It isn't sick! It was ratting in the department store. Hundreds of rats, all of them warm-blooded and running. From now on, my love, we'll eat like kings!"

I swing her around. I'm happy. "I'll cut it," I say. "You go and get some water."

She's really ecstatic, I can tell. She talks on while I sharpen our old knife. This knife is from Before. "Remember the fertility test," she's saying. "Remember the doctor with red hair. There shouldn't have been a lady doing that job. I remember telling you. You were going to say something, but I was called in. I was hoping you'd be worrying with me in the waiting room, but you crept round the side – remember? And you were pulling faces at the window, waving those roses you got me." She giggles at the pale sky and carries on. "I couldn't stop laughing. I was looking at that lady doctor bitch and laughing in her face. When I was given the results I didn't even cry, I was so busy laughing. I'll always remember that day. Will you remember it?"

"Yes, always," I reply, and because I've finished sharpening the knife I send her away. She used to like cats Before, and I don't want to upset her. We used to have two cats. We called them Richard Nixon and Jackie Kennedy Onassis. I preferred Jackie – the tom – but she used to sit all day, just stroking Richard and staring out the window. I hit her once over that cat; I told her to come to bed and stop talking to the damn animal. We argued. I hit her across the face. She didn't stroke the cat any more after that, but she still sat by the window all day.

I make a long cut down the cat's side. I don't bother to skin it, because its fur is thin and it all falls out along the line of the cut. Blood bubbles out from inside but it smells funny, like burning rubber and bad food. I open up the cat. The lining and guts blue-black like tar, eroded and decayed. The cat's mouth is open in a silent shriek. I throw the cat into the sluice. I watch it eddy round in ginger circles before disappearing into the muddy froth.

I go and find her. She is up to her knees in black mud at the edge of the sluice and her tights are lying on the bank. She's singing "Downtown" by Petula Clark. It's the first time in years I've heard her sing. She's got a good voice. I watch her for a while, and then I call to her. She comes running up to me, smiling and singing.

I don't smile.

"What's wrong?" she asks. "Isn't it big enough for both of us? I'll have the bone, honestly I will. You have the cat, it'll be good for you."

"The cat's sick, darling. It's all swollen and purple inside. We can't eat it now."

She drops the bucket. It goes swirling into the sluice and into the deep water. We watch it dully. "I'm sorry," I say.

"Don't worry," she says, brightening up. "You get into your suit. We'll have a nice dinner. I'll put some meat in from that bone I got. That'll give it some substance."

I kiss her. The sluice roars behind us. There's one thing I really love about this woman, and that's her sense of humour. You need to get on top of things.

Her breath smells bad. It's because of the water. My stomach hurts, but I'm hungry. I'll get into my suit, my wife will cook my meal. We're going to have a good dinner.

Nick Gill (16) and Leander Deeny (15)

The Book of Colours

Let it be a lesson to those who come after.

In the beginning, there was Brown. And the Brown was with God, and the Brown was God. And lo, God saw the Urth, and it was good. And He saw that the Urth was alone, and that was not good. And God, in his Brownness, begat six sons from the ether to live with him. And the sons of Brown were Yellow, Red, Blue, Green, Orange and Purple. And God saw that the sons were envious and did great injustice to each. So God, in his Brownness, gave to the six sons, each a part of the great Urth. To Yellow He gave the deserts, and the powers of heat. To Red He gave the mountains and the powers of War. To Blue He gave the seas and the oceans and the powers of water also. To Green He gave the forests and the powers of disguise. To Orange He gave the Sun and all the planets that the Urth circles, and to Purple He did give the air and the ether that did surround the Urth. And unto each of the sons did He give a tribe that would follow them, for, in his Wisdom, He did see that his sons did want to rule.

But lo, God did look down, and He did see that there was a great evil upon the Urth; for man did quarrel with his brother, and did covet his wife, and also his ass. And the tribes of the Sons did fight, and did do wrong among themselves. And God did say "The Sons do quarrel, and in this they do wrong; let the tribes be stricken with plagues."

And on the first day He did send a plague of locusts, and they did eat the grain. But lo, the Sons did say "We have beef! Who has need of bread?" And God was not pleased.

On the second day He did send contagion, and all the

267

beasts of the field did die. But the Sons said unto their tribes "We have stores saved for a time of famine! We will survive!" And God saw that they were unrepentant.

On the third day God did black the sun and dim the stars, and there was not a light in heaven that could be seen. And the Darkness did continue for seven nights and seven days. But the Sons said unto their tribes "We have torches and candles! Who has need of God when we have all that we need here?" And God looked upon them and saw that they had turned their backs to him, and He was saddened.

On the fourth day God created a seventh son, who was White, and to White was given the power of Sight. And God did see that, because White was able to see and perceive all, the other Sons would be jealous. And so God scattered the followers of White around the Urth, and they were all separate.

And on the fifth day, God did create a son. And God looked upon his son, and he did smile, for he was good. And God did say "I have failed, my son. The Sons are uncontrolled and have turned their backs to me. I leave to you, my one true son, the keys to this once great land. I look for the day when Urth can be returned to those who truly care." And God did bless his son and he did go out into the Wilderness from whence He is never returned. And His son did sleep while the Sons did fight.

Patriarch Dreyfus closed the heavy book with a dusty thump, wiped his wire-framed spectacles on his purple robe and squinted out at the rows of impassive student faces that gazed at him. They were, of course, followers of Purple, but they were not yet permitted by law to wear the purple robes of the initiated; only a purple band across the chest showed their affiliation.

"Now, er . . . who can tell us what lessons are to be

learnt from this . . ." His voice tailed off. Dreyfus had a habit of doing that. It was as if his train of thought had arrived at the station, but only a few of the passengers had got off.

A lone hand raised at the back. It was a complex procedure, reminding the viewer of Meccano – the joints were put together well, but seemed to have no control over where they went. The arm was swung vertically, as the muscles seemed too thin to push it up without some help from momentum, and the other hand came across to grasp the elbow, as if afraid that it would fall down unless supported.

Dreyfus carefully placed the spectacles on the end of his bulbous nose and peered at the aerial appendage in the vain hope that it would volunteer some information without being asked. Dreyfus hated having to ask students to speak; this was not because he was a believer in relaxed teaching techniques, it was just that he found recalling all the names rather taxing. His students had cottoned onto this, and had realised that if they strategically raised their hands at varying intervals they could get their teacher so confused that an entire lesson could pass quite quietly and calmly without any knowledge actually passing from Dreyfus to anyone. The hand, still airborne, appeared to have no knowledge of this tactic, as it began to wave slightly, as if attracting attention.

Dreyfus wrinkled his brow with the effort of recall, and a name shyly revealed itself to him. "Ah, er . . . Nerk, is it?"

"Yea, o Patriarch."

This caused a little concern among the other students, who turned to Nerk with raised eyebrows and little smirks playing at the corners of their mouths. Nerk took no notice of them, and looked towards Dreyfus expectantly.

"Yes, er . . . Nerk? Yes. Um . . . what do we learn from . . ."

269

Nerk realised it was up to him to finish the sentence.

"The reading?"

"Yes, the . . ."

Nerk cut in before the pause had time to take hold. His voice had a soft quality, but still possessed an undeniable force that held his audience captive.

"The reading tells us, o Patriarch, that God, in his Brownness, created all things equal, and also that God is disappointed in his Sons, and, believing himself to be of no use to the Urth, created his true son, who will come to us when the time is upon us. He will then come in glory, with justice and righteous power, cleansing the Urth from those who seek disharmony. And the day is drawing near."

There was a pause. Some of the students looked down at their boots and thought, "O Brown? You know those unclean thoughts I had about Ellen the serving maid? I didn't mean them. And I've been meaning to pray more, I promise. I'll start tonight." Patriarch Dreyfus had turned his back to the students, and was sniffling into the hem of his robe. After some minutes he turned back.

"Thank you, Nerk," he said quietly. "That was . . . very moving." His voice took on a slightly more businesslike tone. "Completely and utterly wrong, unfortunately. Does anyone else . . .?"

Another hand raised. "The reading shows that God created Purple above the other Sons, and that by giving him the powers of the air he showed that he was greater in ability than the other sons."

"Thank you, Stimp. Well done. Yes, boys, Purple, our Lord and overseer, was created above and beyond the others, for they were weak of will and sought to be greater than the others. But, because Purple was humble and sought only to serve, God raised him higher, and he is truly the greatest of the Sons. Class dismissed."

Chairs squeaked back on the polished wooden floor,

and twenty-seven teenage boys trooped out of the room. One remained behind. Dreyfus was busying himself with the midday sacrifice, and was strapping the boy down, when he felt a pair of eyes boring into his back. He turned to see a confused face, attached to a body by the weakest of links.

"Er . . . young Nerk, isn't it? What can I . . .?"

The boy unfolded from the chair, and, stumbling, waddling, and reeling his way, approached the altar.

"Patriarch Dreyfus, I have multitudinous questionings to lay upon thee."

Ye God, thought Dreyfus, he talks like the Book.

"Er . . . well, I was just getting . . ."

"I can see; what is the purpose of this . . . pre-prandial rite?"

"Well, er . . . this young . . . er, has offended our Lord."

"And how did this happen, Patriarch?"

"I screamed when he hit me," said the earnest youngster, currently strapped to the huge stone table.

"A terrible offence, you must understand, young . . . er . . ."

"Nerk, Patriarch."

"Yes."

Dreyfus noticed Nerk's perplexed, almost tearful expression.

"Nerk, you are new, are you not?"

"I cannot deny it."

"Perhaps we have been plunging in too quickly with you. Take the day off, lad. Get some . . . er . . . See the, um . . . yes. Good."

"Yes, Patriarch."

He turned, after a number of false starts, and shambled down the paved corridor until he was lost from sight. Dreyfus peered after him, and shook his head. The lad was obviously bright, no question, and he had a voice that the corn would listen to. But, still . . . something . . .

A polite cough brought him out of his reverie.

"Excuse me, Patriarch, but I think the candles will be too small if we hold off any longer."

"Oh, of course; sorry, young Jenkins."

"Quite all right, sir."

"Right, um . . ." Dreyfus struggled to remember the words that accompanied the ceremony. His aged brow wrinkled again in effort. Ah, yes. The knife raised high over the body, and then paused. "Jenkins?"

"Sir?"

"How do you pronounce 'purgatory'?"

Nerk walked down the cobbled street, his wooden-heeled sandals clicking on the pavement. He, too, knew there was something strange about him. He had a childhood; common sense and logic dictated that there had to be one. But, for some strange reason, it wasn't even slightly clear. And he could only remember a father. He suddenly felt a sharp tug on the bottom of his robe, and looked down to see a man dressed in rags grasping onto his hem with a bruised and torn hand, covered in dirty bandages.

"Kind sir, good priest – have you any spare change for a poor wretch such as myself?"

Nerk looked around him, and then, seeing no one else that the comments could have been directed to, knelt down next to the man.

"Why are you begging on the streets?"

"Oh, I cannot be employed, sir."

"Why?"

"Why?" He raised his voice. "The young priest wants to know why there is no job for me!" A few passers-by smiled, and a few laughed at the joke. The man cackled through blackened teeth, broken through age and countless brawls.

"Why can you not be employed?"

The man, looking at Nerk's expression, stopped his laugh, and became somewhat more serious.

"Sir, would you look at my hand? What do you see?"

Nerk looked down at his hand, and then back up to the man's eyes.

"I see a man with a bandaged hand, and a pitiful excuse."

The man smiled ruefully, and looked down at the floor.

"The priesthood says – not that I'll hear a word against them – but I cannot work because there is an infection in me that cannot be cured. This is why I am out here in all weather. This is why I beg for what other people don't need, and I eat what other people throw away."

Nerk looked down at his feet for a while. Then, leaning forward, he kissed the man on the forehead, stood up and walked away.

"Words make poor meals, priest! Kisses fade, but gold is forever!" the man shouted angrily.

"Kisses last a lifetime – words feed the soul," was the reply, and then Nerk was lost in the crowd.

The man cursed, spat on the floor, and rubbed his infected hand. Which was suddenly no longer painful. Startled, he unwrapped the filthy bandages, and stared at the new, baby pink skin that showed a completely healed limb. He stared at the appendage for some time.

"Blow me," he whispered quietly to himself.

Father Dreyfus was waddling down the narrow corridor towards the abbot's cell. Due to his large frame and the corridor's constricting qualities his progress was somewhat limited, and he occasionally paused to pick up paintings that had been knocked to the floor by his bulk. He had been giving some serious thought to the lad Nerk, who

273

seemed to be far too old-fashioned in his approach to religion. Of course, Brown had created the Sons as equal; but, as the clichéd old saying went, some were more equal than others. It was right and correct, and it was obvious to all that Purple was created greater than the other sons. All this old-fashioned equality was very well, but it had to make way for modern principles. Purple was the great Son, and it was right that all those who could not see this simple and basic fact had to be sacrificed to avoid further sin, and thus the loss of their afterlife. However Dreyfus was worried about Nerk. Perhaps a little corrective therapy with the other Patriarchs would help . . .

Dreyfus' musings were rudely interrupted by two large men blocking the passage in front of him. They were wearing the black robes of the laymen, but these two seemed to have a particularly menacing air about them. Dreyfus smiled nervously at them.

"Good morning, gentlemen. Brownness be with you. May I trouble you to pass by?"

The men said nothing, but merely smiled back at him. This did nothing to help Dreyfus, who swallowed nervously, and smiled his glazed smile back at them.

"Gentlemen? Um . . ."

One of the men stepped forward.

"Patriarch Dreyfus?"

"Um . . . yes?"

The man smiled wolfishly; then, as one, two soot-blackened blades sliced through the air and stabbed through Dreyfus' ribs, with a sickening crack of gristle and bone. Then, with a wrench that brought fresh fountains of blood from the holes in Dreyfus' chest, the two yanked their blades free again. Dreyfus slumped back against the wall, the shock apparent on his face; his mouth opened and closed like a floundering goldfish as he stared at the red stains on his palms. His gaze moved from the hideous pits that had appeared in his body, to the expressionless faces of his attackers.

One of the men bent close to him, his breath rancid on Dreyfus' sweating face.

"Ego te absolvo," he whispered in his ear. Dreyfus, in one last moment of clarity, realised that something bad was about to happen to him. Then it did. His dying thoughts were that he should have taken his father's advice – there was a good living to be made from farming.

Nerk, meanwhile, was wandering the streets, looking everywhere, and actually seeing very little. Why was he here? All he could remember was that something big, something important was going to happen. What he couldn't remember was why he was here, or even where he had been before. As he wondered these mysteries, he was unaware of the shabbily dressed man who was following him at a distance of some twenty metres. When he stopped to let a donkey-drawn cart go past, he felt a hand clutch at his robe. Looking down, he saw a familiar face. In front of it, however, was a somewhat less familiar object.

"How did you do it then, eh?" the face wanted to know.

"I'm . . . what do you . . .?"

A pink hand was thrust in front of Nerk's bewildered face.

"How d'you do it?" On receiving no reply, the man shouted out to all the people in the courtyard. "See this young lad here? He healed my hand!"

"Shut up!" hissed Nerk, but the old man took no notice of him.

"See? Good as new it is now!" he cried out, as a few interested bystanders encircled him.

"Infected, that was! Never to work again, they said! But now . . ." He turned to Nerk with wonder in his eyes, as did most of the crowd.

"I . . . well, that is . . ."

"Brown has come," one of them whispered. Another took up the words.

"Brown has come."

"Brown has come."

The whispers became louder and louder as one and all turned to their neighbours, wide eyed, and repeated the words over and over. Slowly the chants died away, as they all turned to look at Nerk, who looked both astonished and embarrassed at the same time. The man threw himself at Nerk's feet.

"At last! He has returned! Lord – what is the true colour?"

"The true colour? I don't . . . well, there isn't . . ."

No one waited to hear the rest of his answer, as one woman at the back of the crowd said, "Surely Purple is the true colour! He wears the robes of a Purple!"

Distracted, Nerk looked down at his robes at the incriminating purple band that ran right across his chest.

"What? No, not Purple," he said, tearing the band from his robe and throwing it onto the floor.

"See, he casts down the robes of Purple! Let us cast down Purple! Down with Purple!" Again, another, and then another took up the cry, until a whole crowd, armed with clubs, bottles and anything they could find, was up and baying for blood – Purple blood, if there is such a thing. They seemed determined to find out if there was, as they all simultaneously ran from the courtyard, screaming and hollering.

In the rush to obey the words of their God, no one actually stopped to listen to what they were.

The Council of Colours was meeting for the eight hundred and twenty-seventh time, and nothing had changed. Item one on the agenda was the persecution of the Pinks.

"What is the problem here, Red?" asked Blue. "It's not as if they're any different to you; they just have . . . slightly different ideas."

"Heretical views and atheistic poison!" screamed Red, spittle spraying all over the Green delegate, who stood up angrily.

"Red, they're exactly the same! They have the same Lord, they have the same ceremonies, they just made it slightly more peaceful and accessible, and not a bad thing too, if you ask me."

"No one did ask you, Green, you bleeding heart liberal pansy!" screamed Red. "By corrupting the sacred words of our rituals, the pagan Pinks have turned their backs on the true Lord and have instead adopted Beelzebub as their patron!"

This enraged outburst from the Red delegate awoke the Orange delegate who had been peacefully dozing at the end of the table. He placed a rather battered old ear trumpet in his left ear, and inclined his head towards the others.

"Um . . . what's the hullaballoo, young, er . . ."

Everyone groaned simultaneously. They could have had quite a good argument if no one had gone and woken up old Orange. For some reason he felt compelled to try and make them agree.

"We were just talking about the Pinks, Orange," said Green.

"Um . . ."

"WE WERE JUST TALKING ABOUT THE PINKS!!" he yelled.

"Oh, good. Who's, um . . . winning?"

"No one's winning, Orange. We're just talking."

"What?"

"Oh, shut up, you deaf old git," Blue said under his breath.

277

"Don't think, I can't hear you, um . . . young Blue, there," Orange warned.

"What are you going to do, mumble at me?"

"Don't think I won't . . ."

"Oh please, can we all keep quiet, here?"

Purple had stood up, and was now casting his gaze over all the assembly. Despite what the Book and Nerk both said, some were obviously more equal than others. Purple gazed down scornfully at the others.

"Red, what appears to be the problem?"

"Pinks."

"The Pinks. Have they, perchance, tortured one of your followers?"

"Um . . . no."

"Something worse, perhaps? Have they killed a Patriarch?"

"Well . . . not as such, no, but . . ."

"I see. Well, it must be something truly terrible to have aroused your wrath in such a manner. Pray tell me what it is." He leant forward, so that he could peer over his spectacles at Red, whose face now almost matched his robe's colour. Everyone else subconsciously leant back. They knew a bad sign when they saw one, and sarcasm coming from Purple was like an air-raid siren for the emotions. Red coughed, embarrassed.

"Well, they've . . ." There was a long pause while Red tried to think of something concrete that the Pinks had done.

"They've changed the words of the hymns!"

"Really? A heinous crime, and one that must not go unpunished, I'm sure. Tell me: what did they change the words to?"

"Well . . . they said, 'Let us praise the Lord Red who is great upon Urth.' "

"I see. What was the original text?"

"The original? Well, 'zÓû ~ } & * & ày, ^ Æ.' is what the Book says."

"I see. And this is what you say at your ceremonies, is it?"

"Um . . . yes?"

"Highly laudable, I'm sure." Red visibly relaxed. "Oh, incidentally – what does 'zÓû ~ } & * & ày, ^ Æ.' mean?"

"Um . . . well, I'm not an expert, obviously . . ."

"Of course. Merely being the head of an Order does not mean that you should know anything about it," said Purple with a smile.

"Um . . . no, I suppose . . . anyway, it means something like, um . . . 'Let the Lord Red, who is great upon Urth, be praised by us.'"

"And the difference between the two translations is . . .?"

Red bridled. "Well, the inflection, and the . . . the word order is totally . . ."

"Yes, yes, but what does it lose in the translation?"

"Um . . ."

"Quite. And what it gains is a greater understanding, not to mention a whole family of vowels."

Red's eyes flared wide open. "Look, Purple, I don't see what makes you so high and mighty all of a sudden! We're trying to be adult about this, and I don't think that your sarcastic comments are helping us a lot here. The Pink Order is merely a breakaway, insignificant sect, and I demand that we crush them under our heel!"

All eyes turned fearfully towards Purple, who was looking strangely shocked. Red decided to press home his advantage.

"Moreover, I think that some justice should be brought upon the leaders of this sect, and that they should have an example made of them!"

Five heads swivelled to look at Purple, who was still

wearing that shocked expression. And, curiously, had a large red stain on the front of his purple robe. He slowly looked down at his front and screamed. Then there was a twang and a hiss, and Purple dropped back into his chair like a stone. All heads slowly turned to look behind them, at the entrance. One of the guards standing by the huge double doors was holding a crossbow, and was grinning devilishly.

"Gentlemen," he said. "I believe it is time for a little chat."

Nerk was sitting on an abandoned orange box, with his head in his hands. He knew everything now, and didn't like it one little bit. He had just unwittingly unleashed everyone in the city on the Purple order, and no one would be particularly pleased when they found out that it was him, a mere student, who had told them to do it. He had to try and stop them. He set off at a run down a back alley.

The bearded man lowered the crossbow, and walked to the centre of the room, surveying the delegates seated in the chairs around the large table. He finally reached the seat where the body of Purple was. He reached down and, grasping the body by the shoulders, lifted the purple band off his chest and hung it round his neck. Then, grinning broadly at the assembly, he said:

"Gentlemen – I believe you have a new delegate."

This was not a wise thing to say, as, at this moment, the entire crowd burst in through the double doors, looking for anyone wearing purple.

Nerk was about three minutes too late. A very hectic three minutes.

*

Nerk was about the three hundredth person to come bursting through those double doors that day, and the dramatic effect had worn off slightly. The effect of seeing around six hundred corpses still had the effect it was intended to have, however, and Nerk staggered back, retching. He recovered his poise after a few minutes, and trod, ashen faced, through the room. Around three hundred crowd members had had a close quarters fight, but that hadn't stopped around two hundred black clothed warriors from firing on them with their assorted weaponry. Here and there was a body pierced with dozens of bolts, and others with mighty slashes across their bodies. Nerk sat down and began to weep silently. The black clothed men had tried to steal the Purple throne, that was obvious; the crowd had come to kill the Purples, that was obvious. Nerk was the cause of all of it.

That was obvious.

Slowly he regained his feet. Unsteadily, he tottered his way to the open window. Shakily he climbed onto the ledge. Gracefully he leapt.

Nerk plummeted to the ground. God soared into the sky.

God rose above the Urth, leaving Nerk behind on the ground. He now knew what had to be done to make Urth whole and pure once more. With the help of his people in Heaven, he could make the Urth great, and call his father back from the wilderness. God smiled to himself, as he finally left the shattered remains of what had once been Urth's greatest city. He could make it wonderful now, he knew.

God found himself pondering how long he'd been gone. He needed to be able to get his most trusted advisors together and begin anew. As he finally rose into Heaven, he could see, far off, a group of brightly coloured people.

Curious, he approached them, and one of them, the one he could now see was dressed in purple clothes, came towards him, and threw himself on his knees at God's feet.

"At last! He has returned! Lord – what is the true colour?"

Siona Laverty (9)

Christina Totty (13)

Life on Planet Earth

In this study of Human life I, *⚙◆*▲▼⚙◻*, will cover a wide selection of unexplored topics ranging from Christmas[1] to Politics[2]. In this second study I report on the interesting but bewildering subject of holidays.

A holiday on Earth can be put into a description of days of recreation or relaxation. A holiday is similar to a hypo-drone suflex ne-gap on Wispa, my home planet. But a human holiday has some unique experiences I hope never to experience.

To gain my information on this subject I used a human contraption called a mini-camera (a large, metal third eye). I concealed it on a human and tried to decipher the strange information I received which did not match with the definition stated.

1 Christmas – festival commemorating Father Christmas's birth; see previous study.
2 Politics – story tellers selling porky pies; see future study.

My problems began when concealing the camera, which took several tries while the human was sleeping[3]. I first concealed it in the human's clothes (a multicoloured second skin which they shed every day). I was unaware that they shedded it every day and lost several cameras this way. I next tried attaching it to a human's arm. This would have worked in principle, but because they cannot shed this skin, they rolled over in pain (an attention-seeking noise when damage is caused), and awoke from sleep swiping at the air meaning that they did not want their arm damaged in any way. I finally managed to secure a place for the tiny camera in the human's watch (a ticking bomb-like device also meaning the verb "to see").

My study starts two days before the holiday. The humans: two larger taller humans, one slightly smaller human and one small human. I planted the camera in the watch of the slightly smaller human who I will refer to by name, No You Can't Go Out. The small human is called affectionately, Shut Up. The two larger humans are adult humans (this means they cannot grow upwards any more, only horizontally). They are called by two different names each, one of them is called Quick Come Look At This or the other affectionate name is Why Not and the other adult is called I've Done What You Told Me Can We Go Home and I Really Like That I Haven't Got Anything Like That.

Day 1
The group of humans are out shopping (an advanced way of hunting; see previous study); they are getting vital

3 Sleeping/sleep – a state where humans practise being dead so that when they eventually die it isn't a shock. Humans don't have much control over it and are often over-practising, causing them, when they wake up, to still be semi-dead.

supplies of clothes (this second skin cannot be naturally grown) and sun cream (similar to ice cream but is not made out of ice and does not, from personal testing, taste as nice. It is deliberately put on the skin, unlike ice cream, and makes the skin go pink).

No You Can't Go Out says to I Really Like That I Haven't Got Anything Like That: "I really like that and I haven't got anything like that and surely I can't go without three swimming costumes?" The adult's reply to No (a shortened personal name of No You Can't Go Out) is "No, you can't have it."

Day 2
The day before the holiday frantic activity takes place in the home (place where humans sometimes eat, argue and sleep). This activity consists of arguing and packing[4].

Quick Come And Look At This and Shut Up seem to make themselves scarce on this day which must be some

---

4 Packing is done in stages. No You Can't Go Out first packs what it wants to wear, second it reconsiders what it has packed and starts again, third it packs the bare necessities and ends up with all its clothes packed and no room in the bag (container which is similar to a wallet, but the difference is that a bag holds socks and a wallet holds receipts[5], but both get filled up with useless things like tapes without tape players and 101 copper pennies[6]) and then, fourth it gives up packing and asks I Really Like That to pack the bags if it seems to know better.

5 Receipts – a slip of paper used in the advanced form of hunting called shopping when the prey has turned out to be poisonous/too small/too big or was broken before it was caught.

6 101 copper pennies – this is a measure of money. (This comes in the form of paper and metal shapes and is more essential for survival than food (fuel) and can be exchanged for anything. What it is used for apart from exchanging and what value it is are still unknown.) Pennies are the smallest lumps of metal and prey exchangers manning tills (oversized calculators) will not accept more than 100.

sort of ancient ritual. They do do packing but not to the satisfactory standard of I've Done What You Told Me.

This day is also used to argue and nag each human in the group. I believe this is to build up the great excitement because tomorrow the humans are going on holiday. You would think the humans would be pleased. It appears not, as is the same with the "relaxing" time of Christmas, it seems to show that holidays seem to cause more stress, worrying and overall general bewilderment than any other working/studying time. The reasons humans go on holiday seems to be a clouded mystery, but perhaps one might be more clear than another. That is that they go to learn about alternative cultures; I will try and prove this theory during the holiday.

Day 3

Early in the morning, when Earth's sun has risen over the world, the humans are rudely awoken by a large Turn That *@!$@*! Thing Off! which makes loud beeps and rings, awakening the humans from their needed sleep practice. Research shows that Turn That *@!$@*! Thing Off! is a very unpopular device causing many decibels of noise, triggering many more to come from various humans. Its task may be to awake the humans earlier than usual so they can catch their plane[7]. Shut Up was awake very early this morning with bags packed and singing[8] very loudly.

7 Plane – similar to bird but migrates for the Summer instead of the Winter. (Summer and Winter are two seasons whose purpose is to stimulate conversation, e.g. "Phew, it is cold" in Winter and "Brrr, it is hot" in Summer ??)
8 Singing – quoted from Bark the dog, "Birds do it, bees do it, even educated fleas do it, let's do it, let's sing a song." This song is accompanied by people climbing up wedding[11] cakes, building bridges and standing on roofs of houses singing this song and holding signs saying "Hollyfox Building Society".

He shook Quick Come And Look At This out of bed (similar to the floor but squeaks more) and tried to do the same to I've Done What You Told Me but was screamed at by a moving lump of bed shouting, "SHUT UP, AND GO BACK TO BED!!!" (Perhaps first inter-species communication between bed lumps and humans?)

By dawn (another position of Earth's sun), three members of the human group were up and re-fuelling. One however was still semi-asleep/talking to a lump and was not dressed in time to re-fuel and wash[9]. All the group were in the car (very expensive umbrella with wheels, which causes the humans not to exercise their legs/cramp/sickness and boredom), and travelled along a road to the airport[10].

At the airport various problems arise.

1) Quick Come And Look At This is confronted by several very large humans in uniform (the same colour sheddable skin worn by the largest, most unoriginal humans) who insist on throwing a pooper scoop, "Cliff Richard's Greatest Hits" (I wish he would hit himself) and diarrhoea tablets (used to prevent filling the pooper scoop) and then slashing the insides of the bag revealing several small packets of talcum powder/salt?? Quick Come And Look At This was then removed in a car with added blue flashing lights for decoration and to warn other car drivers to avoid it as it cannot steer very well.

2) Shut Up is interested in the journey of the luggage as it

9 Wash – a terrible punishment for Shut Up when he has fallen over in a farmyard, or on a cow pat (similar to patting a dog but does not fit in a pooper scoop (scoop for poop) and smells, but not as much as Shut Up).
10 Airport – a place where the contents of the luggage is thrown about violently by a large human in search for small amounts of talcum powder/salt?
11 Wedding – excuse to sell tissues.

travels round the roundabout (moving round about round) and disappears into a hole (perhaps the mouth of a hungry plane feeding on luggage?). Shut Up follows the bags, and also disappears into the gaping hole/mouth. The actions taken by Shut Up cause event number 3.

3) The remaining adult trying to keep order goes into automatic overdrive of functionary systems causing it to stop standing up/screaming/crying/arguing/thinking (I have never actually believed that humans do think, but I will give them the benefit of the doubt)/breathing/living. The adult was removed and taken to hospital[12] in another slightly larger decorated car where humans leapt up and down on its chest using a more advanced and noisier version of Turn That *@!$@*! Thing Off with less results, e.g. no screaming lumps of bed.

4) No You Can't Go Out goes out of the airport carrying large amounts of money and credit cards (plastic measurement of more than 101 pennies) which have been stolen[13] from various stupefied, gormless humans milling around the airport terminal (type of disease which you don't want to catch as it is deadly serious). With these, No catches a plane to a foreign/warm/law-free land where in a later study it was revealed that No had changed its name to Is That Yours Madame? and has acquired (see stolen) one house, five cars, the Spanish crown jewels, a pooper scoop factory and one gerbil[14] called Arrgh It Bit Me!

12 Hospital – place where people die/sleep, and after all that practising it is still a shock.
13 Stolen – the most advanced way of hunting known to humans, involving looking innocent while putting your hand down someone else's back pocket.
14 Gerbil – a shredding machine of fingers/homework (work done at home)/clothes/quilt covers and carpets.

Conclusion

After all this studying I still have not found any reason for a human holiday because it has no links with culture, relaxation and is only vaguely related to pooper scoops.

Translated from Wisparian to English.

Lucy Pawlak (16)

Alexandra Romeo (16)

God and the Devil

God and the Devil sat on a park bench. The Devil
drummed his fingers irritably on the arm of the bench
while a black rain cloud hovered over his head. He was
dark, with a sharp nose, small brown eyes and a thin
mouth from which a half-smoked cigarette hung loosely.
His thinning brown hair was neatly gelled back, giving
him the appearance of a Mafia godfather.

Sitting there dressed from head to toe in a black suit,
he appeared a macabre contrast to his neighbour. But that,
supposed God, was what it was all about – good and evil
– light and welcoming, dark and forbidding. One could
not exist without the other – they cancelled each other out
– they kept the world going.

290

God sighed. He lifted his spectacles off his nose and polished them with a sky blue handkerchief which sat elegantly in the breast pocket of his blue suit and matching waistcoat. He had a sweep of greying hair, pale blue eyes and a rather bemused look on his face, which was strangely youthful.

Birds flew around God's head, twittering sweetly. The Devil looked at them out of the corner of his eye and pursed his thin lips in agitation. He reached inside his black jacket and pulled out a writhing snake. God started slightly when he saw it, slamming shut the book he was reading, *Wuthering Heights*. The snake, its eyes glinting evilly as they caught the sun, twirled itself around the Devil's arm.

God's book had been replaced by *Jane Eyre* and, attempting to ignore the Devil's hissing companion, he began to read.

"I've called him Darren," said the Devil chattily, attempting to start a conversation.

God, totally engrossed in his book, nodded and turned a page.

"The snake," repeated the Devil, determined to get a response, "is called Darren!"

Still no reply. The snake hissed and inched closer to God, spitting angrily at him. God dropped his book, whipped out the blue handkerchief and waved it at the snake.

"Sorry, sorry – the who is called what?"

The Devil sighed and shrugged. "I might as well be speaking Welsh." The snake disappeared in a puff of smoke.

"Now I perceive the Devil understands Welsh," quoted God, leafing through a copy of the Complete Works of Shakespeare.

"What?" said the Devil, not really expecting a reply.

God peered at him over the top of his spectacles, which were now perched once again on his nose. "Henry IV, Part Two," he answered.

"Thrilling."

"You should read more; it's very liberating."

"I do not want to be liberated."

God looked at him despairingly. "Don't you want to expand your capacity for knowledge?"

"No."

"And why," continued God, "do you always have to dress in black?"

The Devil rolled his eyes.

"How about . . .?" The Devil's clothes shimmered and changed into blue jeans, a white tee-shirt and a red waistcoat. The Devil curled a lip and immediately reverted back to his original attire.

"Colours don't suit me. They do nothing for my complexion."

"Why don't you experiment? Be different. Try a black shirt instead of a black polo neck tomorrow – you must be sweltering."

"Shan't."

"Oh honestly." God opened *Tess of the D'Urbervilles* at a bookmarked page and began reading. His chirping birds sat on the back of the bench, preening themselves in the warm autumn sunshine. The Devil's rain cloud thundered loudly. God ignored it.

The Devil stubbed out his cigarette and another one appeared in the corner of his mouth. He blew a lungful of smoke in God's direction. God coughed loudly and glared at the Devil.

"And you know something else you could do? You could lose some of that." He pointed at the Devil's rotund midriff.

"Oh, stop nagging me," complained the Devil.

"No. Mr Motivator's great! I lost three pounds doing his exercises."

"His exercises!? Jumping around like a lunatic and yelling 'Huh!'? Please – spare me!"

God's initial enthusiasm drained away. "You could stop smoking."

"Oh, come on. It's like asking you to stop reading. I mean," he picked up the book, "Paddington Bear? Give me a break."

God snatched the book away defensively. "It's good!"

"So was Marilyn Monroe, and look what happened to her."

"Are you suggesting Paddington Bear is going to die of a drug overdose?"

"Someone might have laced his marmalade sandwiches."

"You have a sick mind," sighed God.

"Thank you."

God decided to persevere. "Try this." He handed the Devil a copy of *It Shouldn't Happen To a Vet*.

"What's this, then?" asked the Devil.

"It's really funny. It's about a young vet in the Yorkshire Dales who has to deal with the most amusing cases. It's not hard to read and you can—" God cut himself off. The Devil was silently burning a hole in the cover of the book. He looked up, aware that God had stopped, and hastily threw the now unreadable book over his shoulder, hitting one of the encircling birds which fell, still twittering, off the bench.

"You are quite the most cruel, evil, illiterate, ignorant and mean person I have ever met."

"I do my best."

"That's a compliment to you. Why do you never compliment me?"

"Not in my nature."

God harrumphed loudly and tried to get stuck into *Jeeves and the Feudal Spirit*.

"OK, OK." The Devil wagged a nicotine-stained finger at God and stubbed out his cigarette. "You are. . . . very good at reading, really good at writing, probably teacher's pet at school . . ." He tailed off. God glowered at him.

"Sorry. You are well-meaning, kind, generous, honest, nice and basically the complete opposite of me."

"In the great scheme of things," said God, "that is the idea."

The Devil took the cigarette out of his mouth and studied the glowing end. God glanced up at him from the pages of *The Go-Between*. He wrinkled his nose at the Devil's right hand.

"You should think about getting that removed."

"What?"

"That." God pointed to a black and purple swastika tattooed on the top of his hand. "I've heard the new laser treatment is very effective."

"Yes, it is getting a little out of date. I should change it. How about . . . 'Yugoslavia – Death'? 'Northern Ireland – Blow 'em up'? 'BNP rules'?"

God flapped at him. "No, no, no! I meant get rid of it. Don't replace it."

"Or I could tattoo a little nuclear explosion going 'Bang . . . whoops!' "

"Oh shut up."

"Ooh, temper temper!"

"Your behaviour is most irritating."

"Well, do something about it, then," provoked the Devil.

"Sometimes I could just hit you!" shouted God.

"Ooh, careful, you don't want to lose your reputation for being Purveyor of Peace, Mr Holier-than-thou! I'm better than you, anyway."

"When have you ever won, in the long run, over me?"

The Devil sniffed. "I nearly won once. I managed to get rid of six million people in six years, thank you very much."

God gazed sadly into the distance. "Those people are with me now – *not* with you."

"What are you trying to say?" asked the Devil.

"I'm trying to make you understand – to comprehend – that good will always win over evil – *always*. And even if you and I end up cancelling each other out completely, and we have to leave people to their own devices – they would work it out. They have faith in what is good."

"Oh yatter, yatter, yatter," said the Devil, yawning.

"It doesn't matter what you think, I'm right."

"You are getting an oversized ego, pal," said the Devil threateningly.

"You wanna do something about it?" growled God, suddenly reminding the Devil of Robert de Niro.

"Fine. Seeing as you're offering, I challenge you to an arm wrestle. Best of three."

"Agreed." They shook hands quickly then wiped them on their clothes. A table and two chairs appeared in front of them. They sat down opposite each other.

"Of course," said the Devil, matter-of-factly, "whoever wins, gets to win on the Middle East as well."

God did a magnificent double-take. "What . . .? But . . .?"

"Oh, you know," said the Devil condescendingly. "You win, they stop fighting; I win, they don't. Quite simple really." The Devil smirked at God.

"That . . . That's not fair!"

"And what are you going to do about it?"

God regained his composure, rolled up his jacket and shirt sleeves and, leaning his elbow on the table, announced, "I'm going to win – *that* is what I'm going to do."

SCHOOL PRIZE WINNERS

Three schools were awarded a School Special Award for submitting work of outstanding quality:

Christian Brothers Primary School, Greenpark, Armagh, Northern Ireland

Kell Bank CE Primary School, Healey, Masham, Ripon, North Yorkshire

Rattlesden VCP School, Rattlesden, Bury St Edmunds, Suffolk

The following schools won School Awards for submitting work of the most consistent merit:

Banners Gate Junior School, Sutton Coldfield, West Midlands

Bedgebury Lower School, Lillesden, Hawkhurst, Kent

Channing School, Highgate, London N6

Chatham Grammar School for Girls, Chatham, Kent

Dalriada School, Ballymoney, Co. Antrim, Northern Ireland

Glenfall Primary School, Charlton Kings, Cheltenham, Gloucestershire

Halesworth Middle School, Halesworth, Suffolk

Handford Hall CP School, Ipswich, Suffolk

Hockerill School, Bishop's Stortford, Hertfordshire

Hoe Bridge School, Woking, Surrey

Marden High School, Marden Estate, North Shields

Milbourne Lodge School, Esher, Surrey

Netherhall Comprehensive School, Cambridge

Newcastle under Lyme School, Newcastle under Lyme, Staffordshire

Newstead Wood School for Girls, Orpington, Kent

Notting Hill and Ealing High School, Ealing, London W13

Oakridge Parochial School, Oakridge Lynch, near
   Stroud, Gloucester
Port Regis School, Shaftesbury, Dorset
Putney Girls' High School, London SW15
Royal Grammar School, Jesmond, Newcastle upon Tyne
Skipton Girls' High School, Skipton, North Yorkshire
Spratton Hall School, Spratton, Northampton
St Anne's Middle School, Bewdley, Worcestershire
St Patrick's Primary School, Armagh, Northern Ireland
St Peter's High School, Penkhull, Stoke on Trent,
   Staffordshire
The Mary Erskine School, Ravelston, Edinburgh
Tregelles the Mount School, York

INDEX

303